C000040621

peterhayden16@gmail.com

*[It's customary to provide a brief author portrait on the back page but by the time you've read this you'll know more about us than our wives do, so I'll leave it this time.*
*P.H.]*

*i*

# CONTENTS

Printed in England. T. Snape Printers, Preston.Lancs PR1 3TY

Tel: 01772 254553

# FOREWORD

Time after time over the last few months a huge wet hand rises up out of nowhere and slaps us in the face: It's Happening.

People were astonished during the referendum when tempers became so heated that families and close friendships were driven apart, sometimes permanently. As with the referendum for Scottish independence. Your place of origin is a special thing: home town, mother country, fatherland. We defend it ferociously. I can't do this politically - I know the arguments, but so what? I'll simply say that mine was a big sprawling family, and the big sprawling smorgasbord of colourful European democracies is my symbolical family. I love it.

So you won't find political discourse in the pieces below - there is fact, sure, but largely it comprises anecdote, recall, and simple fiction. The pieces on Catalonia are the work of my lifelong writing buddy, Tony Tysoe, as is much of the section entitled 'Doing the Yards'. In that respect, it's a joint effort, I've simply put the parts together. His two short stories, Roadside Attraction and When Phillipa Brown Met Ava Gardner, first appeared in 'Catalonia Today' magazine. A number of the passages have also been filleted from the as yet unpublished work, 'We Have Cleaned the Ganges', so regard this as a taster. It will come - stay in touch.

I haven't made a detailed check of the various words and phrases in other languages I've used. I have a long history of murdering the couple of European languages I know, I love it, and don't intend to break the habit of a lifetime here. I don't want the pieces to be polished in that respect - it would be a lie.

So it's probably clear already that anyone with a love of Europe and a few adventures under their belts could put together a similar book. I hope you do. I hope dozens of them appear. Or if you want to send one-off pieces to me, please do. Whether I can propel them into the market depends on uptake of this one, but I'll certainly enjoy reading and responding.

Crazy Horse Press supports indie booksellers. Please don't lend this book out if you can point your friends to one of the recommended online bookshop services below.

uk.bookshop.org
pgwells.co.uk  (Winchester)
sales@devizesbooks.plus.com  (Devizes)
hungerfordbookshop.co.uk  (Hungerford)
fiveleavesbookshop.co.uk  (Nottingham)
pagesofhackney.co.uk  (Hackney)
grovebookshop.com  (Ilkley)
walkersbookshops.co.uk   (E. Midlands)
bookabookshop.co.uk   (Oswestry)
toppingbooks.co.uk  (Ely, Bath Edinburgh & St Andrews)
thebookhive.co.uk  (Norwich)
yellowlightedbookshop.co.uk  (Tetbury & Nailsworth)
mrbsemporium.com  (Bath)
muchadobooks.com  (Alfriston)
city-books.co.uk  (Hove - click/collect only, around
                         Brighton area)

You can also email me to receive an updated list of bookshops and other outlets who in their great wisdom and discernment, currently stock it.

# 1. FANTOFT SOMMERHOTEL - SCANDINAVIA

The coast at Brighton leaves little to the imagination. It's not Pembrokeshire with its inlets and promontories and surprises round every outcrop - it's just a line as far as the eye can see in either direction, with a second line, the skyline, in front. From early childhood I knew that if you stared hard enough at that line you would almost see France.

*     *     *     *

I lost my cherry in Antibes, a few days after England won the World Cup. As we left Dover to hitch south, a Radio Rentals black and white TV in the High Street showed Portugal coming back from three down to beat North Korea in the quarter-final. My memory is vague now, but the bare outline is that when my hitching mate and I arrived, we fetched up in a small campsite of some twenty places in the garden of a bar, and made the acquaintance of two girls from Nantes. My amle and I got their tent, the other two went off to ours. Later there was an interruption from her mother; they were leaving early the following day and she needed her daughter to pack. The zip went up and the tent filled with a huge circle of light. The mother showed every intention of speeding up the process. In panic I started rummaging around for the condom, which was no longer sheathed where it should have been. She directed the torch. 'Ça va, ça va - j'ai perdu ma montre. Je la trouve.' She moved away, distracted by someone. 'La capote anglaise c'est disparu,' I whispered. We hunted blindly until the mother came back and refocussed her arc light, and I had no option but to abandon the task to Monique. To this day I have no idea whether the English hood was found by mother or daughter.

Scorers: Hurst (3), Peters, Hayden (aet).

Two years later, different campsite, different mate. This time Holland, my college friend, a Communist Party member, and I had been arguing intensely for some months about Alexander Dubcek's socialism with a human face: the Prague Spring. And that's where we were heading. Again, we find ourselves in the company of two girls, Dutch, from our campsite. We're walking a wooded path in twilight. One of the girls is distinctively more attractive than the other. Whether they've drawn the same conclusion about us I don't want to say, but the pretty one has fallen into step with my mate. We're walking close together. As night soaks in and the line between trees and sky fades, the girl I'm with sprints down a dip with a small copse of trees giving cover at the bottom. To my surprise, my friend chases after her, and they lose themselves in the copse. So what can you do? I fall in step with the pretty one and after some careful diplomacy we find ourselves compatible. Why? I asked him when the evening had ended. He'd simply not recognised which of them had run off, and without hesitating, had assumed the one he was with, and gone after her. She, the one who ran off, I guess had been trying to gee me into action and found to her delight she'd got the mate. We met up again after breakfast the next day and they asked if we'd heard the news - that Russian tanks had crossed the Czech border. Thus we hatched plan B and reset the compass for Sweden.

I was going to skip over Denmark, which we merely passed through, but as I was writing a memory sprang to mind - we arrived in Copenhagen after midnight to find the Youth Hostel locked and in darkness. Standing together trying to figure out what to do next, rucksacks on the ground beside us, a car pulls up. The chap, bespectacled, maybe late fifties or early sixties therefore we assume harmless, tells us he was the previous warden for this hostel, and because he disapproves of the new policy of locking young travellers out, often does a midnight sweep and puts the stragglers up at his place. We shrug and accept. His apartment is big, the room we are in has bedding on the floor but fine by us. We have a schnapps and a beer with him. He shows an interest in my friend who he says reminds him of Shakespeare's Puk. I can see it - he has a leprechaun's face and short legs. We turn in. Moments later he bounces through to us in his pyjamas. 'My little Puk, where are you?' There's an enthusiastic chase among the bedding and around the room, but we were right, he's harmless, we see him off and get to sleep. So I skip over Norway (of which more later) and Sweden instead, since by this time we're out of money and have to head straight for Gothenburg, and the ferry home.

By coincidence, I found myself in Copenhagen two years later, having fallen deeply in love with a Danish girl who was part of an exchange group visiting our college. She was beautiful in that small-chested, elfin, almost androgynous way that was popular then. Living in her apartment with a partner and young son, which was why she had to overcome a difficult bout of guilt before we took ourselves to bed together. For that reason I didn't take her address when we parted, and she knew not to offer it. But I couldn't get her out of my head. A friend had dated one of the others in the party, and they were corresponding; I wrote via him and his lady a note saying that if her circumstances ever changed I'd be over like a shot. A year or so later, out of nowhere came a note that her partner had been kicked into the long grass due to an indiscretion, and I found myself spending christmas 1970 with her. It puzzles me now to understand the differing tariffs she placed on her fling as opposed to his; I think the key was that he'd taken up with a mutual friend over a period of time, whereas she'd ring-fenced our thing as a little one-off on tour.

At the end of the week I lingered just a couple of hours too long and contrived to miss the ferry, so arrived two days late for the new term in the school where I'd started my first teaching post a term earlier. Obviously my first stop was the head's office. 'You're here then. Did you have a good time..?' Shit - spare me the sarcasm, just hit me with it. 'We covered your classes, you haven't been put down as absent, I presumed you'd need the money.' That was it. No bollocking, nothing, he meant every word.

I never found out if Inge took her guy back. Shortly after, I fell for only the second time in my life, and remain, in love with a girl from a nearby flat just off Ilford Lane. It was the right thing all round, I was nowhere near ready to parent any child, certainly not one from another country whose language I didn't speak. Except for the phrase Gladelig Jul, which she'd written on the back of the vinyl copy of Disraeli Gears she'd bought me: 'Gladelig Jul and all that Bullshit' to be precise.

I'm fascinated by languages, though I don't speak them well. The richness of Europe with its languages and flags, its cultures. Wouldn't the U.S. be a great continent if the states had different flags and languages, and cultures. As they should in fact. Make America great again!

The Norwegians seem to give more weight to religious argot, the French go for defecation, we favour words of a vaginal and aggressively sexual sort - I sense this, but know nothing of course. My wife by this time and I grew tired of our flat on the noisy junction of the Barking Road and Greengate Street, and decided on impulse we would leave teaching and go to Norway for a while. You could do that in the Seventies. Why Norway? Simply that it sounded clean and tranquil and Plaistow felt grubby and loud. So we gave in notice, packed some bags and headed for the Newcastle ferry. The plan, the only plan, we had was to chat people up on the ferry to get some low-down on Bergen, where it was heading. It was hard going until Stavanger, where a large gang of students got on to return to Bergen Uni for the summer term. They took up the floor and chair space of a section of the lounge, got their beers and guitars out, and started singing the Beatles. We were in. By the time we'd completed the short hop to Bergen we were good for jobs, a place to sleep, the loan of a record player, and I had a regular football game sorted.

Our work, and eventually our flat for the next few months, was at the wonderful Fantoft Sommerhotel. Fantoft was the university campus. Probably still is, but I'll do all this in past tense, from our treasured memories. Degree courses were much longer than ours, typically seven years as opposed to three, but with a very long summer break, which was where the summer hotel came in. As students left for the summer, our job as staff was to gut and clean the rooms and prepare them for holiday occupation. Because of the length of courses it was common for married couples to be seen pushing their prams round the campus. Presumably they had places in the town, not on campus. Quite a number of the students either came from Bergen families or found places to stay over the summer, hence the regular football. They were fabulous friends, and took it on themselves to guide us through our apprenticeship in Norwegian life. And also, though they all spoke immaculate

English, made it their summer project to teach us the language. One chap in particular, raided his little sister or step-sister's reading box and read and translated the books into a tape-recorder. Without hesitation, I can still rattle some of the phrases off. 'O lope er et form for sport.' (To run is a type of sport.) 'Dette er et concoransebot.' (This is a racing boat.) And my favourite: 'Hestene hoppe over hoye hinder.' (Horses jump over high fences - you even get the rhythm if you pronounce the last e's, as they do.) From a younger brother I got the gen on argot. The most used was Helvete - hell, or I suppose hellfire. He assembled for me his idea of the worst possible curse: Helvete rompe fees - hellish arsehole fart, which struck me as being on the tame side. In my youth a French friend did the same exercise and came up with, Putin bordel de merde - putin (prostitute) is used as the expletive fuck, so fucking brothel of shit. I tried it years later when a guy nudged me coming out of a side road, it seemed to do the trick.

Incidentally, coño, or cony, is the Spanish/Catalan word for cunt. My ex-pat Spanish friend is married to a Catalan, and we have used this salutation with each other since I was reliably informed by him that it was a common word of endearment in his (new) parts. I challenged him. No, really Pete, my father-in-law regularly uses it with me. Hmm.. He presented me with a Barça top on my sixtieth with the slogan 'El Cony Afortunat', the lucky cunt, presumably because I was still playing. I suppose we do use it here from time to time – 'How are you, you old cunt?' but exclusively between men, whereas according to my friend it's acceptable to women too, but more likely to be of the older generation, and probably rural.

So we spent a blissful summer in Bergen. The woods just beyond Fantoft with their graceful larches and spruces also had a profusion of wild raspberries and bilberries which we'd pick and eat as we walked, or sometimes collect and take back. Often Bergen summer rain was that minutely fine type that a friend would call wetting rain, and we'd find ourselves gathering in the special quiet it brought with it. There was a small wooden stave church there, only accessible via the various footpaths, like something out of a folk tale. We walked the woods in midsummer, on midsummer night itself and other nights close to it, among the hedgehogs and bats, and utter stillness, not the smallest leaf moving at all.

My wife was a stuepiken, a chambermaid, and I was a baggage hand and general gopher. One has to be wary of national stereotypes, but, let's say certain differences raised their heads. I went to help a coach load of Germans with their baggage and room location. It was a low building (everything was built low), three floors. They figured out which floor they were on by the room numbers, formed a line, each a yard or two apart, from the coach to the third floor, men and women - they were all elderly - and passed the cases up the line chanting the floor numbers as they did so. My job, simply to take them from the landings to the rooms and collect the tips. Americans were casual and compulsive tippers - I had no idea back then that life in the States runs on tips until I called to an American in a bar I was working in some years later to give him the small change he seemed to have forgotten. He cussed under his breath and pulled out a couple of pounds to give me, on the assumption he hadn't left enough, and I had the right to call him out. It was common at Fantoft for travellers from beyond Europe, particularly Americans, to be on tours of the 'Ten Cities in Fourteen Days' variety. There were no Euros then, only national currencies, so they must have had wallets full of kroner, francs, lira, pesetas and so on to navigate their way through. I actually heard the old saw: 'Are we in Vienna, I thought it was Thursday?' One poor old boy flustered in his pockets for a while and came up with a fistful of coins and notes and begged me to help myself. He didn't know what currency he was holding, what it was worth, and what the tipping norm for this particular place was. He was in distress. It was poignant, I couldn't mug him.

My wife experienced a similar national behaviour range. The Dutch she found would invariably service their own rooms even to the extent of turning down one corner of the bedding, in the house style. This would sometimes occur even on their last day, when they knew the entire bedding would have to be stripped off and laundered, with the addition of a neatly folded tip on the pillow. Americans would typically drop everything where they stood at the time and head off for the day. She (Sue) was called in to be disciplined on one occasion - one of the Americans had accused her of stealing a pair of trousers. This is not an exaggeration. She said naturally she'd hung them in the wardrobe, where they were found. There are two incongruities here: that she should have stolen the trousers rather than simply whatever might have been in the pockets, and that the occupant hadn't considered looking in the wardrobe before making the accusation.

Spirits were forbiddingly expensive in Norway, and it was quite common for students to set up their own stills for brennevin, firewater, which they flavoured with rum or brandy cake flavouring. The local supermarket was well stocked with these, whereas the strawberry and orange comprised a small fraction of the stock. It was clear what was going on, it seemed to be tolerated on the same basis dope is today - OK as long as just for personal use.

The local paper was the Bergens Arbeiderblad, roughly the Bergen Daily Worker. Maybe there were others, there must have been. The Arbeiderblad ran a kind of 'In Town This Week' feature, and they latched on to us after a while, I think through student contacts. Sue had an art background and was keen to draw some of the fish in the town aquarium. She asked if she could buy a kind of season ticket, but when they found out why she wanted it, they ushered her straight in and said she could come and go as she wanted for the summer. 'Porno and Western in our Cultural Desert' the column headline went. She was a girl in her early twenties at that time who simply wanted to sketch some fish; no problem - they bounced off this to target consumer capitalism. I was working on some children's readers at the same time, so became the subject of another article. Yes, I'd been teaching in the East End, and yes, had been modelling these harmless primary readers on the wonderful Nippers books by Leila Berg; this was enough for the headline, 'Frustrated Teacher Writes Books for Working-Class Children'.

Decades later, when our daughter was at college, a communal meal was organised. There were students from several countries at the table. At the end, without forethought she said Takk for maten to the cooks, and started collecting up plates. A face suddenly turned to her, a Norwegian face. 'What did you just say?' It had been a daily phrase in our house since she was born, she hadn't fully registered it was in another language. Thanks for the food.

So there's a hundred thousandth part of us which will always be Norwegian. That makes me want to sing.

## 2. DOING THE YARDS - BELGIUM

The Yards – the First World War Cemeteries – visit has been a very special trip involving myself and two friends for a number of years. We have always stayed at the same place in Ypres, run by a Flemish couple who treat us like family, except for one year when I was unable to come and they opted to stay at the Toc H place in Poperinge instead. I said I would only ever go once, after the first time, because to me the place, Flanders, has an almost mystical feel about it, but that was a promise I didn't keep.

Poperinge, incidentally, is the origin of my favourite Belgian beer, Poperings Hommelbier, 7.5%. It's also famous for a couple of other things. There is a plaque on the wall of A la Poupée cafe in tribute to Eliane Cossey, or Ginger, acknowledging the fact that Ginger gave great comfort and reassurance to our boys on the Ypres Salient. One officer wrote: "A sweet little sixteen-year-old girl came to serve us. I fell a victim at once to her long red hair and flashing smile. When I asked her name, she replied 'Gingair' in such a glib way that we both gave a burst of laugher. We had a splendid dinner, with several bottles of bubbels, and Ginger hovered delightfully about us." The three of us read gleefully, shamefully between the lines and enjoyed making up our own drunken versions. There is now a statue to Ginger in the town centre. Poperinge is also famous for Talbot House, Toc H, a much-shelled and derelict hop house which was turned into a refuge and chapel for war weary troops by an army chaplain, Philip 'Tubby' Clayton. Because of Tubby's very sympathetic and comforting way with the traumatised boys of the front, from time to time a deserter would find his way to Talbot House.

I don't want to malign Tubby, but my understanding is that after sharing their horror stories he would find them a warm place to sleep and pass their names up the chain of command. The place where deserters were shot can also be seen in Poperinge, a single brick cell looking onto a small walled enclosure with a post at one end.

The first Yard we ever visited together was Polygon Wood, early one morning as the sun was rising. It was completely quiet and breath-taking. Polygon Wood has two levels, the higher one with an obelisk, the lower one a smallish field with the rows of immaculate classical marble headstones, enclosed by the wood. I still can't quite account for the clout of breathlessness and reverence I experienced that first time. We sat without speaking on the plinth for some minutes, then Pete and I found ourselves descending to where the headstones were. Later we were aware of voices: our other friend Tony was gesticulating as if trying to express something just out of his reach to a group of cyclists who had appeared. They were Dutch it turned out, he had obviously been trying to express some ethical point in words both he and they could understand, or had possibly wanted to explain the feelings to them that were in his heart and mind as he sat looking down on a scene that conveyed utter peace and barbarism at the same time.

What had engaged them however, the group of cyclists, was that at such an early hour they had already visited four 'yards' – they were hoping to take in as many as thirty through the day. Their English more perfectly correct than one can imagine almost any English person speaking in another language, but in this case, not only was le mot not quite juste but their motivation too, both slightly, perfectly wrong. And so from then on it was our tasteless code to refer to visits to this region of absolute sanctity as 'Doing the Yards'.

*    *    *    *

Tony himself had scoured the area some years earlier looking for his grandfather's burial place, and it was he who had initiated our visits:

I FOUND OUT A LOT about my father's childhood very late on in his life, after my mother died. Boxes of papers he didn't seem to have much interest in ended up in our house. There were photograph albums too, loose envelopes stuffed with letters and notes, newspaper cuttings, old coins, tickets, cards, birth and death certificates. A lot of the stuff was in an old Clarks shoe box, but there were ancient leather suitcases as well, with their lids strapped on because the hinges were broken. I began to take an interest.

One thing that caught my eye was a close-up photograph of a wooden cross in a muddy field, with dozens of other similar crosses behind, fading into the sepia-hued distance in neat rows below a wide, cloud-filled sky. Stencilled onto the cross in the foreground was: In Memory, R.I.P. 2nd Lieutenant L Tysoe, 39th Labour Coy. Killed in action 31.5.17. The photo was in a little cardboard wallet. On the inside page was printed, and completed in black ink: Director of Graves Registration and Enquiries begs to forward as requested a Photograph of the Grave of:

| | |
|---|---|
| Name | Tysoe |
| Rank and Initials | 2nd Lieut |
| Regiment | Labour Company |
| Position of Grave | Mindel Trench Military Cem, St Laurent Blangy |
| Nearest Railway Station | Arras |

At the bottom of the page was printed in small letters: Owing to the circumstances in which the photographic work is carried out, the Director regrets that in some cases only rough photographs can be obtained.

My mother died early in 1992. Later in the year I made arrangements to attend Expolangue in Paris the following January. Expolangue is an annual exhibition of new language learning methods, technology, and schools. I decided I would drive there, and on the way back to Calais to catch the channel ferry I would try to find my grandfather's grave.

The day after the exhibition ended, suffering with a sore throat and a hangover, feeling slightly feverish, I gave breakfast a miss and checked out of my hotel early; it was a grey morning, wet and cold, but the traffic was lighter than I expected and I made it past the Périphérique and through the banlieus without problem. There was an open road in front of me. After an hour or so I stopped at a service station for a coffee and a nap but still arrived in St Laurent Blangy, now more or less a suburb of Arras connected to surrounding built-up areas by a complicated network of motorways and main roads, well before midday. I drove into the town straight off the main road. There was nobody on the streets and the shops were closed; when I passed the Mairie I saw that it too was closed. It was a public holiday, and I had not realised it.

At the top of the main street I saw a signpost marked Cemetery. I followed the direction of the arrow down a quiet residential road and found what I was looking for; inside the iron-gated enclosure, most of the polished marble tombs bore coloured photographs of their occupants. None of them looked old. For the most part the photographs were of prosperous-looking figures, stout burgomaster-types. This was no English village church-yard, nor a military cemetery. I left after only a few minutes, feeling foolish and uncertain. Outside, I saw a man head down and pushing a bicycle along the pavement. He and I were the only people in the street.

Excuse me please. Is there another cemetery near here?

He raised his head slowly and looked at me as if I was mad. What?

Is there another cemetery near here?

He swept his free arm in a 180-degree arc. Where have you been? What sort of cemetery do you want? There are hundreds of cemeteries round here. He gave me a challenging look, lowered his eyes and went unhurriedly on his way.

I drove out of Sant Laurent Blangy not knowing in what direction I was heading. I had gone less than a mile when I passed a small roadside cemetery, enclosed by a flint wall. I knew it was a cemetery because over the top of the wall I glimpsed two long rows of white grave markers. I pulled onto the side of the road, walked back to the entrance, and went in through the gate.

The grass was cut short and was springy beneath my feet. The headstones, I saw now, were identical in shape and size, rectangular slabs about a yard high with rounded tops, set a few inches apart from each other in continuous earth beds planted with small shrubs and heather-like plants. There were two rows of them, about fifty in each row. The beds in which they were set were freshly turned over, the grass borders neatly clipped. On their other side, against the opposite wall of the cemetery, a stone cross on an octagonal base rose to the sky.

I stood still for several moments, surrounded by silence, feeling as if everything had stopped. I was dismayed to discover I wanted to cry. I didn't cry, but I wanted to. I wondered for a few moments if I was more ill than I had thought. I went slowly up and down the rows of graves, reading the inscriptions on each headstone. At intervals I stepped back and narrowed my eyes and looked along the length of the rows; the stones seemed to merge into each other and become a single luminous surface. I did not see my grandfather's name on any of the headstones. I told myself I had not really expected to. At that moment, it didn't seem particularly important.

This was the first commonwealth war graves commission military cemetery I had either seen or entered. It was the first of seven in total I visited that day, all within a few miles of St Laurent Blangy, before I got back in my car for the final time and raced north to Calais in time to catch the last ferry back to England. By then I was cold, hungry and feeling definitely ill, but triumphant and excited to a degree I couldn't easily explain to myself, but had to be because at the seventh cemetery I visited, I had discovered my grandfather's grave. By then, obviously, finding it had become important.

I got back in my car after visiting that first cemetery, drove on for a short distance, and saw another one – much bigger. I stopped the car by the side of the road again and walked back to the gates. The silence was the same, the same low walls enclosed the site, the headstones were the same but this time there were several hundred of them. I wandered up and down several rows, wondering if I could feasibly look at all of the inscriptions. Back at the entrance, I noticed a metal box set into the wall. Inside was a visitors' book, and some information about the cemetery. Many of the visitors, I saw, had come to pay their respects to a very great poet – Isaac Rosenberg. I found his gravestone, different from most of the others in that it was inscribed with the Star of David rather than a cross.

Each cemetery I visited had the common features of classical design, careful upkeep and unmistakeable sense of peace, but each was different too. I learnt as I went along. One of the things I learnt was that the sites were regularly visited by relatives of the dead. I felt I was not alone.

The sixth cemetery I ended up at, a few kilometres out of St Laurent Blangy, was the largest I had seen so far. By this time it was getting on in the afternoon, it was very cold and the light was beginning to fade. I was in two minds about whether to stop or carry on along what I thought was the right road for Calais. At the last moment I stopped, and followed the by now familiar ritual of walking back to the gated entrance from where I had left my car at the side of the road. There was the same low enclosing wall, the same cross at the far side of the cemetery, but in between many more of the uniform white tablets in their neat rows than I had seen before. I calculated there must have been over a thousand of them. Too many, I thought. I turned back, without having gone through the entrance, but stopped to open the metal door of the box set into the wall which I knew by now would contain the visitors' book and information about the cemetery. Inside this one there was something else too: a copy of a map, in what I thought was 1920's style, showing all of the villages and cemeteries in the area. St Laurent-Blangy was marked, and a couple of inches away from it to the north-east the Mindel Trench British Cemetery.

The map was useless in all respects except this one: it showed the position of the Mindel Trench cemetery relative to St Laurent-Blangy and the surrounding villages. None of the present-day road network was featured. Nevertheless I felt I had been given a lifeline as reward for my persistence and it would be ungrateful to turn it down. I would borrow the map for an hour or so until I had found my grandfather's grave and then bring it straight back. Nobody would begrudge me that, I told myself, but I felt like a thief as I returned to my car, and I took care that the map was concealed under my jacket in case anybody was watching.

It took me another two hours to find the cemetery. For much of that time I knew I had to be within half a mile of it, but none of the features on the map coincided with those I could see around me and whenever I thought I must be getting close, the road I had to follow would lead me in a wrong direction. At one point I left my car and spent twenty fruitless minutes traipsing along a ridge across a grass field, expecting to see what I was looking for emerge from the gathering gloom at any moment. My frustration levels rose. Finally, I found myself for the third or fourth time back on a nondescript road leading out of St. Laurent-Blangy, lined with houses, garages and small workshops. I left my car, and walked along the road. I stopped another passer-by and asked him if there was a cemetery near here. He shrugged, a familiar Gallic shrug, and walked on. I continued along the pavement for another few yards before I noticed a narrow grass path between two houses. At the side of the path was a small dark green sign on a metal pole. Mindel Trench Cemetery was printed in white lettering on the sign. I walked up the steeply-sloping path and into the cemetery. Minutes later, I was looking at my grandfather's grave, wondering how I was supposed to be feeling.

*     *     *     *

The last time the three of us went to Polygon Wood the approach was being given major landscaping it appeared with a view to setting up a visitors' centre with no doubt toilets, disabled parking and the rest that goes with Disneyfication. We don't go there now, but the Mindel Trench cemetery is still a simple square field, it hasn't been chosen, and we make our way to it each time.

The visits have become arduous for Tony since he relocated to Spain, he has to fly to an airport which calls itself Brussels Charleroi, some thirty miles out of Brussels, hire a car and make the hundred-odd mile cross-country trip to Ypres. On one of our last tours his drive back to the airport was a Tysoe masterclass:

April 2015 (email): "For much of my journey I was 100 percent sure I was going to miss the flight. Conditions on the motorway were horrible. It took me ages to get going roughly in the direction of the A25 and then I found myself on it heading for Calais. I sorted that out eventually but around Mons I took a wrong turn and ended up fuck knows where. It was dark, pissing down, the car was aquaplaning there was so much water on the roads and it felt like the trucks were out to get me. I thought my head was going to explode. Somehow it ended up okay but I'm still not sure how."

Some drivers prefer to rely on maps rather than a satnav. Until recently I was one, a Baden Powell kid, the stars and a simple road atlas as my guide. But Tony relies on neither. Is it fanciful to ask whether he needs to battle his way to and from his grandfather's burial place? I can't say. He is over and above all a man in the Wills and Burke mould.

# 3. 6bis RUE DES GENÊTS - FRANCE

I've had a love affair with France since I was seventeen and used to tune to Europe 1 and follow the fabulous songs of Gilbert Bécaud, Jacques Brel, Sylvie Vartan, Charles Aznavour, in the hope that some kind of simple absorption would get me through A-level without too much revision. On the same basis I found myself sitting in a cafe in Montmartre in spring 1964, Gauloise and copy of Le Monde, looking down my nose at the English tourists.

From 2005 to 2016 we had the half-share of a house in the village of Nizon in Brittany. Brittany is a special part of France, very traditional and self-contained, very Celtic. Our patch was the south coast of Finisterre, Cornouaille, though I've always thought of it as equivalent to Wales rather than Cornwall. It makes no difference really, in that Brittany is part of the Celtic caliphate, a string of misty folkish countries and regions of north-west costal Europe, incorporating Cornwall, Wales, Ireland, the Isle of Man and Scotland. As you drive into any town in Brittany you pass the board announcing their twin towns - all from the caliphate, never English no matter how much easier the exchanges might have been. Apart from a religious commonality, their unity is musical, their common instruments the harp, the pipes, drums and tambours, and the bagadou, the droning bagpipes that are the high feature of every festival. Summer is the season of pardons and fests noz, the musical parades that take place in every town and village no matter how small. Their significance is in the marrow of every community - tourists come in their thousands to watch, but the festivals are wholly for the community and are conducted completely unselfconsciously as if no-one else was there. Each year new young-sters will show up and take their costumed place in the bagadou bands with absolute pride, and as night falls villagers link with each other by their little fingers in huge circles and move slowly round to the music in short shuf-fling dance steps, their arms rotating in half-arcs, reminiscent of bringing in the nets.

The festivals generally feature visiting bands from neigh-bouring towns and villages marching under their historical banners - the bigger ones such as Quimper have march-pasts of maybe a couple of hours with bands from every part of Brittany. I found the Quimper festival breathtaking, but there were others on a similar scale, the Concarneau Fillets Bleus, and the huge Lorient Inter-Celtic festival featuring exclusively Celtic rock and folk bands. If you want to see the Dubliners or Sinead O'Connor one more time before you die, that's the place to go.

There are also what could be termed harvest festivals, huge scoffing parties of salmon, oysters, cherries - what-ever's prolific in that particular region; otherwise simple evening supper gatherings with crepes, and paper-plated scoops of mussels frites, or merguez frites - merguez the spiced lamb sausage found throughout the region and held in such esteem that the newspaper of south-west Brittany headlined and shamed a producer who'd bastardised his merguez with pork.

We didn't have broadband, but there was a little community place of limited opening times next to the public toilet, le Cyber-Espace. I would go and check emails and football scores at the modest cost of 75 cents an hour. The room was dark and unventilated and I seldom managed more than thirty minutes before bailing.

One evening I got there just before closing for a quick check and found a publicity email from the organisers of the European football championships that were being held in France the next year. I had a quick look. I was under a little bit of pressure actually, the only other person in the room was an overweight local lady, a heavy breather who was loosing off little strings of flatulence, little doubles and triples that kept sitting me up with a start even though their volume was low. But football trumps (ahem) les pets in my world and I worked my way through the email. With a French bank account you could make a pre-payment and enter the ballot for tickets. On impulse I did this, shut down quickly and got out into the fresh evening air.

A few months later I came up with two tickets for the Austria - Iceland game. This seemed like a very dud fixture and I was disappointed. No-one knew then that Iceland would send England home and reach the later stages, followed by a large percentage of their total population whose social and maybe genetic closeness is such that several thousand could utter an uncoordinated wolfish chant in complete unison.

The tournament was a great opportunity for us to spend some time in Paris with our son and his partner. We did the galleries together and watched games in the central fanzone, with the illuminated Eiffel Tower as a backdrop. Our game was at the Stade de France, and as my son and I were approaching the stadium a car pulled up and a smart French guy in a suit got out and asked if we were heading for the match. He had some tickets he wanted us to have. He was agitated, he'd pulled up illegally and it was a major route out of Paris. We thanked him and said we had tickets, but he said, no, these were the best tickets, silver corporate tickets with the best view, and he and his friend weren't interested in the game. We shrugged and took them, he wasn't selling them, and he dived back into his car. We looked them ,over, they seemed genuine and were three times as expensive as ours. So we decided to keep them and try and sell the others, but couldn't get a sniff, we couldn't give them away. I went up to a young steward and said ring a couple of your mates and give them these, but he couldn't, couldn't risk being sacked. So we went in with four tickets in our hands. The silver seats were brilliant, just above the main Iceland section the players ran to at the end, having won again. The celebrations between them and their fans were electrifying. The tickets I'd got in the ballot had been in with the Austria fans, who in contrast had become extremely sour by the end of the game. A crazy, lucky experience.

Nizon, incidentally, is part of the commune of Pont Aven, where Gaugin with fellow artists spent his Breton years. The breathtaking little chapel in the woods between the two communities, the Chapelle de Tremalo, has a wooden ceiling reminiscent of an upturned boat, with diabolical, bestial gargoyles at the ends of the purlins so the joins disappear into the bared teeth of these creatures. The chapel also has, hung crucifix-style to the wall facing you as you go in, the original yellow christ of Gaugin's painting.

On the scale of religious belief I'd place myself at the militant atheist end. On the concept of soul and spirit I have a more fluid view, and standing here in the chapel as I am right now in spirit, yes, in my imagination, sure, but I feel myself in its presence again - I'd like to introduce the concept of 'thinness' that seems integral to the Celtic world, that a close friend put to me as we rambled together in a remote part of Wales. If you tried to give a dictionary definition it would read something like, an environment of vibrant spirituality, of human absence, a place where the earthly and unearthly meet. But it defies the definition the minute you open your mouth to make it. But how about this - after many years when the notion remained undefined and dormant in my mind I came across a wonderful description of thinness in the book 'Mary Webster' by Colm Tóibín, which I was reading on a plane, a beautiful book in many ways but quite tedious, when I came across this - I think it's in the last six words but I'm quoting more: the character's on a remote beach in Ireland in the winter - "There was hardly any colour. The world in front of her had been washed down… It was the world filled with absences. There was merely the hushed sound of the water and stray cries of sea birds flying close to the surface of the calm sea. She could make out the sun as it glowed through the curtain of haze… For the last two days she had stayed by (her dying husband's) bedside. But he was already far away from them, so far that they might have been like shadows, people already lost to him. Maybe he could only imagine them all as vague presences, the ones he had loved, but love hardly mattered then just as the haze here now meant that the line between things hardly mattered."

I don't know about the rest of the country but trocs, puces and vides greniers are a massive Breton pastime and a friend of ours would come over for a week or so most summers, would buy himself a small booklet which gave the dates and venues of every flea market, car boot and bric-a-brac sale in the region and set himself a schedule. He had a roomy car and would go back home with it so tightly loaded there was no room for drink. We went to some with him, I had passable French so there was a role for me. He would come over to me and point to an item. Ask him how much it is. I'd say, just point to it and say combien. He'd say, no, go on, you know how to do it. So

I'd say Combien. The guy would say something like Huit, it was obvious what he was saying. Pete would say, offer him six. I'd say, Pete, just say 'six', it's the same. (We're both Pete - he's the friend from the Yards.) You do it. OK – 'Six monsieur'. Oui. He says yes. He'd pull out the money, find my wife Sue and say, Look, Pete got me this for six.

She got the bug. There were a lot of people getting rid of quirky, tatty stuff, and after a brief Skype she and our daughter decided to launch a new start-up called Breton Blue. I was the negotiator, an honorary role: she'd spot something, scrutinise it, get an idea of the price and shake her head and walk away. I'd be skulking out of view. She'd come over: third table down, green enamel kettle, they said ten. I'd go along and turn over several things, ask some prices then offer four and agree five. I got into it and started giving them cheek, telling them their precious family heirlooms were plastic, and other outrages, it was all fun, all a wind-up. On genuine loft-clearance stands rather than trade stands, it was usually the woman who'd handle sales since much of the stuff would be her kitchen and sitting room items. The chap would sit at the rear in a collapsible chair, in his eyes overseeing, in his wife's, doing fuck-all. I'd start knocking her down and when we reached the sticking point I'd say I don't want to deal with you any more and call the husband over. He'd invariably shrug his shoulders and say Oui, OK 'sieur, only to be slapped on the shoulder and told to stay in his chair.

Often the same people would turn up at different trocs, they'd spot me and say, Look out, here comes the Englishman. At one, in Scaer, there was a very jumbled stall where among the clothing I spotted a copy of 50 Nuances de Grey. I think it was Grey rather than Gris, because Grey is the name of the character. I picked it up for a skim to see if I could manage the French. With an arch look the girl said, 'Ça vous plaît monsieur…?' I laughed and asked had she read all three titles, or just this one, and after a bit of banter wandered off. On another stand I picked up a riding crop for fifty cents, took it back to the first stand and told the girl to put it with the book.

We'd get back home to England with a car so full I couldn't see out of any window except the front.

They were wonderful summers. There was an annual open-air festival, les Vieilles Charrues, the Old Ploughshares, which we'd go to. At one I especially remember, it rained the particular gentle variety of soaking Brittany rain throughout, we were drenched immediately, but the music was wonderful, it seemed to integrate into the ambience. I think people sometimes listen better in the rain, they just hunker up and focus on the stage. Joan Baez – her beautiful unpretentious presence and to our surprise decent French, almost unheard of for an American entertainer (or American anything, why should they?); London Grammar, their slow lugubrious songs perfect in the conditions. We should have left right then and made it back for a late one in our local bar, but Lionel Richie leapt onto the stage: 'Hey – here's the mega-star ya've all been waiting for, clap ya hands!' and we stayed for a couple of numbers from curiosity. It was like watching Bruce Forsyth. In fact I claim Sue hasn't seen him live, we'd worked our way so far back she had to watch it on screen – I pushed through enough to be able to say I'd actually seen him perform, I don't know why, a kind of geek thing, and we took our soaking selves home, car heater on full blast.

## 4.  TELEFONICA (Allegro) - SPAIN

After my friend and his wife sold their house, filled their car - a green Renault Laguna bought in Kidderminster, four years and 90,000 miles on the clock, for £3,500 - and headed for her Catalan homeland, his first emails were short. They had no broadband or landline at all, he would pay for half-hour slots at a café, hopefully a little less airless than the one I would email from in Nizon. Setting up a phone service obsessed him, he was dealing with post-Franco desk-wallahs, they were masters of their arts. He began to keep a log, a sort of combat log from the front line, and the following paragraphs are from his emails, plus some passages from the log:

October 4 2004 (email): 'Weather here is fantastic, in fact everything here top hole except for communication diffi-culties. Phones don't work properly and we're finding the dreaded cybercafes a nightmare. If we don't get the phones sorted in short order I'll be topping myself. The pace of the days is amazing – up at some disgraceful hour, long lunch, then non-stop trying to get things done from 4.00pm till 9.00.'

October 12 2004 (log):

The day following the completion of our house purchase.  Request Telefonica to give us a telephone line. This is done by speaking to someone who could be anywhere between Barcelona and Bombay, using the Attention to Clients number: 2004.  During the course of our splendidly constructive conversation I point out that the nearest telephone pole is about 200 yards away, but that previous enquiries to Telefonica by our agent on our behalf had met with assurances that any delay in connection would be minimal. The charming operative laughs airily, tells me not to worry, gives me a case number, and promises tip-top care and attention to all our communication needs for ever.

November 19 2004 (email):

'The days seem to pass very quickly. Currently we are in the middle of getting central heating installed. The house is a total mess, rubble and plaster and brick dust everywhere, quite depressing. Still no telephone, which is a major gripe, but there is a smidgeon of hope on the horizon. Telefonica have agreed to ask the council for permission to put up a post, and we are assured by our friendly local councillor that they will agree, but as for dates – that is another matter. I've played my first match in the San Feliu de Guixols Tennis Club inter-club championship (over 50's section) and won, much to my surprise! The first set was 7 – 5 and lasted over an hour. Mucha Guerra was the verdict of the gallery – I have some oddity value at the moment.'

(A curiosity: Tony played for the E team at our local tennis club and was sometimes partnered when he wasn't on tour by Robert Plant. He never quite got his head round being phoned by him: 'Tony? Rob here, Malvern away isn't it – who's driving?')

December 3 2004 (email):

'New beds arrived today, the central heating is on, and we officially moved into the house yesterday. I'm resident in Spain now, Rosa is back on the books as a fully paid-up Spanish citizen again, with an unemployed husband as dependant. This confers certain useful rights on both of us, which I'll explain during our Christmas visit. It feels like we've both taken a long walk through the dark night of

Spanish bureaucracy and are now just emerging into the light of day. It ain't been easy in a lot of ways, but I'm looking forward to better times ahead. To date probably the best news for me is the progress with Spanish and Catalan, which I'm really getting in to. Reading the papers is a bit like being in a sweet shop – there are so many things on offer that are new and taste great. Catalan culture is no longer the closed book that it was, that's how it feels.'

Some time at beginning of December (log):

Man of few words arrives in BMW and says that he is come to do a feasibility study in connection with our request for a telephone. Paces the distance between the nearest telephone pole and our house, several times. Scowls. Writes some figures in pencil on the back of an envelope. I ask him what he thinks. He says it seems complicated. But is it feasible, I ask him. Yes, he says. Drives off in his BMW…

# 5. ROADSIDE ATTRACTION - SPAIN

FROM OUR HOUSE on the wooded slopes of Les Gavarres it's half an hour to drive into the centre of Girona: fifteen minutes crossing a broad, flat-bottomed valley and then dropping a thousand feet by narrow mountain roads to sea level; ten minutes cruising a section of the fast, straight highway that links Girona to the coast; and five minutes more weaving through dusty suburbs before finding a final parking space somewhere beneath the towering walls of the city's Barri Vell.

I make this journey every day and my favourite part is crossing the valley, where low-roofed stone masias shelter behind copses of eucalyptus and pine set amongst the vineyards and wheat fields. This winter two peregrine falcons have settled here, familiar silhouettes now as they wheel and turn from dawn to dusk on the warm up-currents.

All through the year Africans arrive from somewhere on bicycles, to work land much richer than that which they have come from, but which will never be their own.

It must have been at the beginning of December when the first puta came. A few days later she was joined by another. They stood at a well-chosen spot on the coastal highway just before the airport turnoff, at the edge of a bamboo grove and near a track leading to an abandoned farmhouse where clients could turn off the road and park undisturbed. They wore short skirts, and knee-length boots, and tight colourful pullovers with satin jackets.

One morning the pretty one caught my eye as I passed, and waved. It was a curiously commanding gesture she had probably brought with her from her home in another Europe, I thought. As I considered this I nearly knocked off his bicycle an African pedalling slowly along the verge. I saw him wobble in my slipstream. The reproach in his eyes lingered in the rear mirror as I continued on my journey.

The putas brought white plastic chairs from somewhere, and then replaced them after Christmas with more comfortable ones, upholstered in fake red leather. Once when I went by, the tall puta was sitting on the pretty one's lap. They had their heads close together and were bent over what I guessed was a mobile phone, but it might not have been. They looked happy, and seemed to be laughing. Sometimes I only saw one of them and felt anxious about the one who was missing, though I told myself such a feeling was quite ridiculous.

In our garden at Les Gavarres we have hoopoes, attracted by the acorns from the cork oak trees. They are exotic-looking, but Arabs consider them unclean birds because they foul their nests. The putas, it was soon obvious, were fouling their nest too. By late January, carrier bags were hung out like washing from the bamboo behind their chairs, plastic water bottles lay on the ground, bits of toilet paper flapped in the grass. But in the snatched glimpses I had of them they stayed fresh-looking, untainted by this squalour.

One sunny morning in late February I saw as I went by that the pretty one, who normally wore her thick chestnut hair lifted up off the nape of her neck, had removed her pullover and satin jacket. The green bikini top she was wearing, unknown to her of course, was the same colour as my wife's. Later that day, in an idle moment, standing on the third floor of the Faculty building and staring out over the roof tops of the city to the snow-crested Pyrenees in the distance, I decided the difference I thought I had detected in the way she had looked at me may well have been due to her eyes unconsciously reflecting unanswered questions in my own.

I stopped without planning to the next day. I was returning home later than usual, around 7 o'clock. The sun was down and the putas had gone. I pulled into the side of the road and walked back the fifty yards or so to where the fake red leather chairs were where they always were, set at the same angle to the road. It was a curious thing, but the cars that were passing made no noise. The only sound was the rustling of the bamboo, stirring in the evening breeze. I felt as if I knew the place well but was seeing it for the first time.

I saw the bicycle, thrown down carelessly on its side behind a bush a few yards from the chairs, and then I heard them. A woman was singing softly in a language I did not recognise, a man was making low noises which were not difficult to understand. I took, I don't know why, a few steps forward, and parted the bamboo screen. The pretty one was on her back and gazing at me from over his shoulder, smiling. She said something. The other one raised her head then and looked at me without interest. The three of them were adrift in a sea of trampled bamboo, it came to me, holding on to each other for survival. The dirty mattress was their lifeboat; I wondered how the putas had got it there.

I may have cried out, I'm not sure. As I stumbled backwards the African rolled sideways suddenly and turned to me. Again I saw the reproach in the eyes of a man I had wronged.

That night I slept badly and dreamt of fantastic-looking birds with plumages of bright green and pink and other lurid colours. In the morning I had a fever and phoned the university to say I would need some time off work. Three days later, when I drove past the spot where the putas had stood, by the side of the bamboo grove just past the airport turnoff, they had gone, and they have not been back since. But the peregrine falcons are still in my valley, and the Africans still arrive on their bicycles all through the year.

# 6. EUROVISION

Nothing sums up the colour, exuberance and random-ness of Europe like Eurovision, the major international song contest where national entries sing in pirate costumes (12th), Napoleonic costume (1st), vampire costume, in a pool of satin blood (13th), in tall conical hats, courting a unicyclist with wings (6th), on top of sixteen-foot poles (9th), in latex death metal ghoul masks (1st); where the Grannies from Buranovo sang in the language of Udmurt to raise funds for their church (2nd), Conchita Wurst sang in drag with a full beard (1st), and the Burlesque performer Dita von Teese perched herself on a grand piano flexing a cane (20th). Where voting on merit has been outlawed and countries gang together to stack the votes in favour of their neighbours, usually similar countries of small population and no money who then get the chance to host a great international party even though their song was crap, which otherwise they could never do. Actually, on a personal note, I watched the Mercury Award short-list last night and trust me, Eurovision songs are OK. It's also a contest which the UK can never again win, in recognition of our smug imperialist and now Brexit identity. But hey, we inflicted Sing Little Birdie on them, what goes around comes around. Although it's a definitively European contest, it admits Australia on the grounds that their third most populous city is in Europe. Not a just-next-door country. Australia. In fabulously over-the-top performances spangled with pyrotechnics and massive key changes, half the entrants sing their hearts out for their country, the other half take the piss.

Welcome to Europe.

During the Nineties a friend I worked with, a happily unattached friend, came in on the Monday morning with great news. He and a few mates had got on to a new party, the Eurovision party. He ploughed on through our indifference to sketch an outline of this party, which was basically a hard drinking affair where participants got a competing country, sourced its national drink, and filled the glasses with as much of it as they could get down in the time the song was performed. What energised him in particular was that the draw that year had favoured Scandinavian and Slavic countries whose drinks were mainly vodka-based, and by about nine o'clock they had all been wasted.

Our children were young and most of our friends were couples, so I dropped a memo in the cranial zone marked 'pending' and let it lie for a few years. I finally put it to my wife as a millennial project now the kids were in their teens. In ensuing negotiations I had to agree that it would be a food as well as drink party, and on that basis we kicked off in 2000 and it has run ever since. It was to be understood that the winners would host the following year's party. Variations quickly emerged. National colours and items of costume started to appear. At one of the early parties, the couple who'd drawn Germany arrived early and covered the chairs with beach towels. Busy, or lazy, couples would improvise on food and drink. One year a couple representing Malta came with some bottles of Marston's Single Malt beer and a large bowl of Maltesers. Not very classy really - surely malt whisky if you're going to take the liberty of improvising.

Another year, the couple who were due to host scratched at short notice, so we took it on for them to keep things going. We'd moved house and had had months of alterations. I agreed to do both the food and drink as my wife was at full stretch to get the place ready. On the day of the party I was still involved in DIY and touching up until late afternoon. I dived unshowered or changed into the car, went to the supermarket and got some jars of little bell peppers, humous, and on impulse, a packet of dried apricots. In the drinks aisle there was nothing Romanian but I chanced on a bottle of black vodka. When an ice cube was added it became green; people were impressed I'd gone to so much trouble to source the drink. The food became a plate of humous-filled peppers with finely chopped onion and apricot, drizzled with port. Your Romanian does love an apricot.

In general, the women tended to be the perfectionists - I wonder, was there a bit of culinary rivalry there? Fabulously prepared exotic bites would be brought round, about the first half-dozen being savoured and appreciated, but as the evening drew on they were more likely to just be stuffed in and washed down with drink. The blokes, by contrast, would find the appropriate bottle of drink and plonk it on the table. The year we were Iceland my wife found a recipe for blueberry vodka, but it required the blueberries to be steeped for a couple of months, like sloe gin. She'd left it too late, it stressed her and she went back and forth through the internet looking for a second choice. I told her to get a shower and leave it to me. By the time she was out I'd been to the shop, wazzed up a punnet of blueberries, some sugar and a litre of Vladivar in the blender and got it in a jug. It was sweet and toxic, if a little mushy. We were well down the order and by that time people were necking their drinks without too much concern over the precise recipe anyway.

Occasionally a non-alcoholic drink will turn up. This happened one year when I was getting way too hammered, and in danger of not completing the course: a beautiful swan-necked teapot of Bulgarian apple tea, it was a life-saver. We also rigged the draw one year, the only time, to allow for our friends' grandchildren who were with them for the weekend to get Israel and come round with a jug of fresh Jaffa juice. There is, it has to be said, some-times a song-length pause if not all the countries have been covered, where one gets the choice of taking a breather or having another glass of the previous drink.

There are misunderstandings among newcomers. One couple who got to host thought they had to cover the vacant countries themselves if they couldn't gather up suffi-cient guests. They did food and drink for eight countries. They gave their young son one to do - Italy - bottle of red and a large tray of pizza which they'd helped him make. But took their eye off the ball while he was cutting it. Pizza was a big favourite of his: the guests got a postage stamp-sized piece each and he hid himself off for the rest of the night and scoffed the lot. Newcomers tend to bring way too much of everything, they want to be asked again, and haven't calculated how much food and drink twenty-four couples can assemble. One year we invited the couple who ran our high street deli. They were good party people; they drew Romania. We did tell them not to go to town, but they were concerned about their reputation. They ordered some expensive cheese from their supplier, tried a recipe, didn't think it was adventurous enough, ordered more specialist stuff and made something else; and bought two Romania national football shirts from the internet, one ladies, fitted. Fortunately they were early in the order so could at least relax once they were done.

I've always made it a point of honour to down every drink no matter what and eat every food sample. The 2006 party I remember was hard. Half of the food seemed to be raw fish of one kind or another soaked in dill oil or kindred substance. Not that I can talk - this was another year when I did both food and drink, a year when it was our turn by chance to be Malta, and I made a legit dish of tuna and capers. Malta got one point the whole night thereby winning me and Sue last place prize of Ferrero Rocher plus a couple of Turkish delights for some reason. About half-way through someone came up with a plate of stinking pilchardy stuff, and true to plan I took some and stuffed it straight in before I could change my mind. It seemed a bit bony and I made the mistake of chewing instead of just swallowing, realised if I didn't get rid of it I'd heave, so went out to the back lobby and spat the whole mouthful in the dog bowl; in a blur it shot out from nowhere and wolfed the lot.

The following year's party was dramatic. Such is the party's status that it must take place even if there is a major rival event. In 2007 the event was the F.A. Trophy final, the first competitive game to be held at the new Wembley, Kidderminster Harriers - Stevenage Borough, and our town emptied itself to be there. Therefore, for what we thought would be the one and only time, we videoed it and the party was held the next night. Guests were under instruction not to in any circumstances check who'd won. All went well until there was a power cut. We plunged around in the darkness for a while, picking up whatever food and drink we stumbled across, and finally had to abandon the evening, leaving everything for the next day. By about 4am the food was gone, along with the kitchen. A ring on the electric hob had been left on and when the power came back it had caught some packaging alight and spread through the room.

But you never know what's just around the corner, and in the year 2010 we found ourselves at a second video-taped party on the Sunday, this time in a suburb of Kassel. The occasion was a town twinning visit, and because most of the party gang were involved we had exported it to Germany. They didn't quite get it though, and no matter how many times I had repeated and simplified the rules, on the night a large table was spread with food and drink, there for people to help themselves as and when they felt like it. We had made our part of the draw before travelling, so that at least some preparation could be done, and passed on the undrawn countries for them to do the same. They had ignored this and told their guys to chose whichever country they wanted. I had got my host to take me round a number of shops in the Turkish quarter until we found a bottle of Albanian wine and some native salami, only to find two other Albanias proudly waving red and black flags who had simply come with a few beers. Bloody chaos.

We had all, all the Brits, obeyed the embargo on checking for the result. None of us knew or cared about it, to be fair, and we were in Germany in any case, but as chance would have it Germany had won, and there was a sense of suppressed excitement in the air. About halfway through the drink began to work its magic on the inhibitions and one of our hosts sidled up to me and blurted the result in a drink-whisper. In fact she was expressing sympathy, bracing me for the woeful revelation of the UK's last place and Germany's first, which she thought might be a party breaker. All true fans of Eurovision know this is a perfect result, which I conveyed enthusiastically. My informant could only stand back and admire my grace in defeat.

Here, national characteristics raise their head again. Heads? The concept that Germans are humourless is grotesque, all our many German friends find the same daft things funny that we do and love setting people up and ribbing them. There's a specific genre of humour implicit in the Eurovision thing though. If you scrutinised it the sub-text would be something like: we can't win, the tournament's crap, we never put our best bands out, they wouldn't demean themselves. Let's trash it.

You could say that belongs to the great tradition of lampooning, or that it hints at a side of Britishness that I think it's fair to say Germans in general don't like, an over-critical, mocking, sarky side disguised as humour. Me personally, I love Eurovision as probably the best party of the year, and I'm including New Year's Eve. As host you don't do a thing, just provide glasses and plates and it takes off like a rocket - so I simply leave that other thought out there. I have found over the years though that during the more sober third of the evening I've started to appreciate the incredible effort and choreography the acts put in, and it might be nice to have a change from the smug and sometimes quite xenophobic commentary of Wogan/ Norton or their younger less measured replacements. National character is always elusive though. Some French friends were once telling us of their experiences of British reserve, our reputation for coldness. I said I didn't think we ourselves were reserved nor were our friends, and they said, alors, that's because you're not typically British…

Out of the blue, in May 2011 I had an email, from my result-whisperer. "And Pete: Last Saturday night you might have feel that I was with you. I had a great Eurovision party at home with six friends and a lot of European food and drinks. And I was England!!! Remembered so many times to our Party last year!"

It just takes a bit of faith and patience once the seed has been sown.

## 7. TELEFONICA (Adagio) - SPAIN

January 31 2005 (email):

'Last week the weather was arctic – never seen anything like it, said the locals. It was down to minus 12 last night, pipes froze up, heating broke down, etc etc. That was a low point actually, because it became very apparent that the house is not built for cold weather. Yesterday, however, normal service resumed with lovely sunshine and beautiful blue skies. I spent the day in the garden. I've cleared a patch for the olive grove (always wanted an olive grove, if you remember) and another patch for a vegetable garden. It was fabulous.'

Feb 16 to Feb 28, my birthday (log):

Daily phone calls to Telefonica for more care and attention. During the final call am told that planning approval has indeed been received and passed to local Telefonica headquarters in Girona. Particularly charming but rather loose-tongued operative lets slip that the engineer in charge of the case is one David X. I smell blood.

March 1 (log):

Single handed, I storm Telefonica headquarters in Girona. Initial entrance is obtained by standing outside the front entrance, waving a piece of paper at the uninterested platoon of uniformed guards who can be seen moving backwards and forwards deep in the interior, shadowy and vaguely sinister figures. One of them ambles forward eventually and looks at me through the smoked plate glass of the door. I hold up the piece of paper, shout the name of David X, and begin reciting the books of the Old Testament in English. When he opens the door a few inches I change demeanour and tell him I am an English journalist come to interview David X on an important matter involving the future strategic direction of the Spanish telecommunications industry.

Ten minutes later I am talking to David X in a stairwell somewhere in the bowels of Telefonica H.Q. Preliminary skirmishing over, we both relax and start to appreciate this somewhat surreal meeting. David X informs me that my case is far from unique, that manfully though it tries Telefonica's mission is impossible, and that in his view it's a miracle the whole network hasn't come tumbling down long ago, for want of sufficient resources promised but never delivered by a succession of perfidious governments. Once he gets into his stride, his sincerity is palpable and I fear he is heading towards a depression. I steer him gently back to my own case. He tells me he will retrieve our file, disappears up the stairs from whence he came, and returns after a few minutes, bearing the file. He opens it in front of me, and begins to read. As he does so his brows pucker, his mouth purses, sucking and clucking sounds emerge from somewhere inside him; when he looks up, I can see the prognosis is not good. I steel myself for what is to come.

The good news is that in its wisdom Telefonica is disposed to extend the telephone network to include our house, has requested planning approval for the two necessary poles, and has indeed received notice of approval from our town council for the same. The bad news is that notice of approval has been sent on a form that is several years out of date, and includes a demand for two hundred and something euros of tax which in those days Telefonica was bound to pay. But not these days. Such errors are not uncommon, David X informs me sorrowfully. Town halls are sadly all too often incompetent, in his experience. I can see he is trying to comfort me. I imagine a solicitous doctor informing his patient that the particular terminal illness he is suffering from is much more common than he might have imagined, and that he therefore should not be unduly upset about having contracted it.

As we stare mutely at each other in our dusty and gloomy stairwell our saddened eyes reveal a shared understanding of the difficulties life continuously puts in the path of the unwary. I have come close to loving this man, unlikely as it sounds.

David X rifles through the file again. He extracts another sheet of paper, scans it, and exhales on an airy up note, surely indicating triumph. He waves the paper at me. Telefonica, it seems, has already replied to our Town Council, politely pointing out the error of its ways, and requesting an amended notice of approval form. I must not despair, David X informs me. The amended form surely cannot be long in coming, and once it has he, David X, will personally take charge of the case. Now that my problem is in his hands, I am all but home and dry. As I emerge into the sunlight amidst the pleasant and civilised architecture of Girona, I reflect that I have spent the last hour talking to tip-top service made incarnate.

## 8.  ENGLAND v ANDORRA - SPAIN

But life for Tony wasn't just desperado with Telefonica. He was a big Kidderminster Harriers fan, and we had passed many pleasant seasons on the town-end terrace slagging off away teams' goalkeepers, before he moved abroad. It was an era when you could change ends at half-time, crossing over with the visiting fans as you made your way round, this meant that goalkeepers underwent ninety minutes of treatment rather than the customary forty-five, and fans seemed to be well-informed on their domestic circumstances. Our favourite was a chap called Ryan Price, Macclesfield. Ryan was one of those keepers who liked to wind up the crowd, flicking little V-signs in response to the chants we aimed at him, over-celebrating their goals. He had a monster of a chin, a real ski-slope. But had it shattered in a game at Woking, and was out for a season while it was reconstructed with titanium plates. That would have been a lot of titanium. Then to our astonishment, resumed playing, the game at our place being his first back. The terrace wits were in a quandary, it felt wrong to get at him what with his new jaw. He got a sprinkling of applause as he made his way to the goalmouth, which he reciprocated. It was all wrong. There was a period of rumination. Finally:

'Hoy, Ryan. Cosmetic job was it?'

Normal civilities resumed…

Out of the blue Tony was catapulted from the base of the football pyramid to its absolute pinnacle:

21 March 2007(email):

I CAN'T BELIEVE THIS AND YOU WON'T EITHER BUT THEY TELL ME IT'S HAPPENING

Sorry guys, I just have to share this with fellow Aggborough diehards and other footie fans from my previous life. I've got the job of English language announcer at the Olympic Stadium in Barcelona for the England – Andorra international next Wednesday. Can you believe it? I can't, hardly.

I think they may have got me confused with someone else but I'm not about to let on. What a hoot, eh? I have to be there for the training sessions as well and should have the opportunity to pass on a few tips to Steve and the lads. I'm wondering whether to recommend 2-3-5. What do you think? Who's in the hole if we play with a Christmas tree? I'm worried they'll catch me out on that one.

Well, that's it. Dining out's never going to be the same again.

*      *      *      *

29 March 2007 (email):

I CAN'T BELIEVE IT BUT IT REALLY DID HAPPEN

Hello Chaps,

Sorry to have made you recipients willing or otherwise of my indecent excitement regarding recent events at the Estadi Olympic as we locals call it. A pleasure shared is a pleasure quadrupled is my selfish angle on things. Also, I'm still not 100% sure that yesterday happened, so perhaps if I write it down I'll quintuple the pleasure as well as convince myself that it did. And if that's a load of bollocks – well, maybe I owe you an account of the full story anyway. Here it is:

I've got to know a bloke here who besides being a free-lance photographer is a friend of the President of the

Andorran football federation. The Andorran football federation, so far as I can see, consists of two men, one woman, and a dog. When it was decided that Andorra would play their England match in Barcelona, Tomas, the President, asked my friend Jason if he would help out, acting as a go-between with the English camp for the three days they were to be in Barcelona. He also said they would need an English language announcer to double up with the normal Estadi Olympic announcer, who had no English. Enter me.

Originally I was to be at the stadium all day but on Tuesday I got a phone call saying I didn't have to show up until 4.00pm on the day of the match. Which I did. For the next four hours or so I helped Maria, the Andorra federation's press officer. Around 6 o'clock things started to get busy, and by 7 o'clock it was total chaos. Maria's English was so poor she couldn't seem to grasp that my name was Tony. She kept calling me Tyson until the very end of the night.

Amongst other images engraved on my memory are Mark Lawrenson in the middle of a strop because he couldn't get into the press room when he wanted to, and Garth Crooks looking lost in a huge empty space somewhere underneath the stadium pleading for somewhere better to do the post-match interviews. There's something disconcerting about looking into a face which is both that of a stranger and very familiar to you. I felt my puzzlement was being reflected back to me, but that might have just been paranoia, of course. I mean, there's no way Garth Crooks could know me, is there? Lawro's features close up, by the way, are best described as very puffy.

A lot of the chaos was down to reporters not having the right UEFA accreditation for one reason or another. They all had to queue up to get their passes from Maria, who at the same time was trying to cope with 101 other problems. It got to be hilarious. There were two little Japanese who nobody could understand and were kept at the back of the queue for two hours. There was a German guy who just needed one key for an office so that he could move his team's camera. It was classic – he kept getting passed from one person to another and then to another and then back again to the first one. Nobody seemed to know who was who and in charge of what. At one point he – the German guy – got it into his head I was from the English FA. By 8 o'clock nerves were pretty frayed. The stadium was filling up, there was a lot of noise from the English fans, nobody seemed to know what the arrangements were for the national anthems, what time exactly the teams would come out onto the pitch, etc. There was a bloke from Sky who looked like Frankie Howerd and had the most contemptuous sneer on his face I have ever seen, continuously. He didn't have to say you couldn't organise a piss-up in a brewery – the sentiment seemed to flow from out of him in a wide sweeping current. The guy from the Sun, as another example, wasn't happy with the place in the press area he'd been allocated. Maria told me to tell him the view would be very good. When you're watching England the view is never good, he replied, quick as you like. These guys are seriously hard-bitten, in a very English way if I'm allowed that comment. In part it was a cultural clash and it made me feel quite nostalgic. Maria was actually lovely and the I've-seen-all-this-shit-before attitude of the press people was endearing in its way too.

About 8 o'clock I had a meeting with Xavi, the stadium announcer, and was told what I would have to do. He would do a welcome in Catalan from the pitch-side, I would do it in English, he would do the Andorran team sheet, I would do the English. We would then move to the press box for the rest of the match. I was there principally in case there was trouble and an announcement needed to be made in English. The instructions went something along the lines of: 'If the English hooligans start shitting us, you tell them to stop.' I told them I'd got the idea. He asked me if I'd done this before. I told him I hadn't. 'Novato,' he said, clearly not impressed. 'Can I do the English substitutions please?' I asked. 'If you like,' he said. I got the impression that I was there on sufferance so far as he was concerned.

A word about the stadium. Actually, and completely coincidentally, I'd wanted to go to this stadium for some time because it features in my current work in progress. It was built in the 1930's on top of Montjuich, a hill on the edge of Barcelona with a great view over the port and the rest of the city. The inside of the stadium has been completely modernised but the outside has been faithfully preserved. It holds about 55,000 and is beautifully symmetrical – really very nice. It's three tiers open except for one covered side. The reason I'd been interested in it is that it was going to be used for the 1936 Workers' Olympics. The 1936 Workers' Olympics were a protest about the Olympic Games being held in Berlin that year. People came from all over the world to attend, but on the day the Games were due to begin, the Spanish Civil War started. It's a little known event, but very poignant I think – the Workers' Games I mean, not the Civil War. In my work in progress I've got an account of a bloke cycling from England to take part, who ends up fighting in the war. Anyway, all that's got nothing to do with football.

There were apparently 20,000 people at the match – 99% of them English, I should think. The number amazed me. On the motorway driving into Barcelona in the afternoon we had passed three or four cars that had obviously driven from England. I mean, driving to Southport on a cold wet Saturday morning to see Harriers play a league match is one thing, but driving to Barcelona to see England play Andorra… what is it with these people?

The cross of St George was draped everywhere in the stadium and the fans were making a right din, I've got to say. Most of them had been drinking, but there was no real trouble that I could see. Twenty minutes before kick-off I was still running around between various groups of people with last-minute problems or needs and then suddenly everything happened very quickly. The teams were on the pitch, some presentations were being made, then Xavi was doing his welcome and then, a couple of yards in front of baying England fans, I had my mouth against a mic and was saying Good evening everybody and a warm welcome to the Olympic stadium here in Barcelona for this Euro 2008 Group E qualifier between Andorra and England. Just like that – smooth as you like. Piece of piss. It was actually an amazing feeling. It was so effortless but the volume was so vast – it felt like being in control of a really powerful car that would do amazing things at the slightest tweak of the controls. Then the team announcements. All OK, smiles and thumbs up, then the match started.

Xavi and I were in a brilliant spot, just behind the English dug-out with a completely uninterrupted view. I can tell you straight off that England were completely crap. It had been drizzling for most of the day and the pitch was very slippery but honestly we looked SO ordinary. Andorra were totally useless apart from at falling over and fairly thuggish into the bargain but you'd have expected us to show a bit of flair. We didn't. After about 20 minutes of abject passing the ball around in front of 11 Andorrans to no effect, the fans really started to get stuck into the team, and McClaren.

What are they singing? What are they singing? Xavi kept asking. I found myself translating 'McClaren is a wanker', 'You're not fit to wear the shirt', etc. It was concentrated venom, and impressive in a way. Every ten minutes or so there was another message from the police asking for an announcement requesting people to sit down, stay in their particular enclosure, not block the gangways, etc., which I duly made. As you might imagine the effect was minimal, but so far as I could see at least the announcements didn't provoke more rowdyism.

Individual players were targets too. Every time Downing got the ball he was booed. Robinson came in for loads of stick as well.

At half-time, when McClaren walked from his dug-out to the tunnel, there were drunk fans really screaming at him and straining to get to him. He was ashen. While he delivered his half-time talk, I had Cava and canapés amongst some very elegant looking people.

We improved after the interval, especially after I substituted Rooney. That, I've got to say, was possibly the highlight of the evening for me. For a mad moment I really was tempted to say Iysden Christie instead of Jermaine Defoe but good sense prevailed, as it usually does, more's the pity.

Rooney was totally useless during the time he was on the pitch. You could just see that he was a negative influence on the team. He had a couple of nice touches, but an equal number of fluffs, and spent the whole time in a sulk, quarrelling with his marker. On that performance, he's a liability. Jason told me that on the Tuesday one of his duties had been to go and buy a new play station for Rooney because he'd thrown the one he had against his bedroom wall and broken it in a fit of temper. This is not a joke.

From where I was sitting it really was possible to get a much better grasp of the way the game was being played than it is standing behind the goal, and also to judge the performances of the players. No doubt this is obvious, but it really struck me last night. Gerrard worked hard all night and his second goal was a beauty. But he made a pathetic dive in the box to try and get a penalty. Lennon looked dainty and made some good crosses under pressure. But I tell you what – this is nowhere near a good team.

When we got the first goal, from the celebrations of the players you'd have thought we'd won the World Cup – a bit pathetic really. I mean, this was Andorra, not Brazil for heaven's sake. The fans were baying as well, like Romans seeing the lions get their first Christian, I thought, and hungry for more.

England supporters, by way of observation, are an ugly looking bunch. Most of them are skinheads. It might not be politically correct to say so, but a lot of them looked in-bred to me. Perhaps they are. Perhaps they never look for a mate outside the English supporters' tribe.

On the way out of the stadium there was some chanting of No Surrender to the IRA, Rule Britannia, etc. but nobody said anything, least of all me. All the way down the hill from the stadium to the Palace of Montjuich there were fans pissing by the side of the road. Not pretty.

# 9. WORLD WAR 1 INTERNMENT - GERMANY

My grandfather was born in Schwäbisch Hall, formerly Hall, south-west Germany in March 1878, the eleventh of twelve children to Friedrich Karl Heinrich Kayser, baker and hop-master, and Friederike Christina Ungerer - of whom two didn't survive childbirth, one died at the age of two, and two didn't survive their teens. In the Old German papers and documents I now have thanks to the wonderful help of Andreas Maisch of the Schwäbisch Hall archives, the first child to be born has the word 'spurius' against its name. The word for illegitimate, out of wedlock. Not many spurius babies survived beyond the first week in those days. Hall was the old German word for salt, most houses had a salt-pit in the garden, it was a source of instant wealth, and my grandfather Ernst's grandfather produced the Holz Gerüst, wooden pit-props that were used in the digging out process. Sometime around the turn of the century Ernst emigrated to London and became eventually a chef in a hotel in Kensington.

The German population in the UK by 1914 was about 53 thousand, half of whom were living in London. Their typical trades were bakers, butchers, shoemakers, tailors, carpenters, skin-dressers, skin-dryers, sugar bakers – i.e. sugar refiners working in boiling houses where everything was coated in a thick treacle of black grime – musicians. Many had reached London on their way to the United States and decided to go no further.

There was the usual reaction that comes with waves of immigration – that they took jobs, kept wages and working conditions down, lowered the character of their neighbourhoods, were people traffickers and brothel keepers.

Prince Albert was nicknamed 'the German pauper'. The 1864 Street Music Act was aimed at prosecuting German street bands. Hostility increased after the Prussian defeat of France in 1871, and was stoked by Kaiser Wilhelm II's support of the Boers. The Entente Cordiale with France was declared in 1904. The 1905 Aliens Act gave immigration officers the right to inspect steerage-class passengers of incoming boats to remove undesirables and deny entry, having 'a great effect in excluding disease', the Home Office said. There was hostility to the German naval build-up. Germany was the noisy neighbour that needed to be reminded of its place in the food chain.

*      *      *      *

The Aliens Restriction Act and Defence of the Realm Act were passed days after the declaration of war in 1914 requiring all Germans to register immediately at a police station, prohibiting them from areas near ports and industries, from ownership of firearms, signalling equipment, photographic equipment, cars, motor cycles, radios, military charts, maps and handbooks. Pigeon keepers were compelled to kill their own pigeons. "Every effort must be made to kill a bird seen flying across the North Sea. It might be quite as important for the crew of a warship to bring it down as for them to hit an aeroplane" (Racing Pigeon magazine). Travel of more than five miles without a permit was prohibited and searches and checks for firearms and questionable materials and activities could be made. German social institutions were closed down, German civilians were subject to a 9pm curfew.

Days after these restrictions, all Germans between the ages of seventeen and forty-two were required to be interned; this was immediately rescinded by the War Office.

Mass arrests had begun but there was the huge, simple problem of where to put them. The shortage of accommodation was 'the kind of thing which one would expect to find in a Gilbert and Sullivan opera'. Kitchener didn't want the war effort to be diverted by the supplying and building of camps, and the guarding of inmates. The available space was in any case becoming necessary for POW's – combatants rather than civilians. Prime Minister Asquith backed off: enemy aliens would be dealt with 'instalment by instalment as soon as, from time to time, the War Office authorities are able to provide for them'. There were many exceptions – vicars, doctors, invalids, those who might be valuable to the war effort, those in education, 'races hostile to Austrian rule' such as Serbs, Poles, Croats, Czechs. Many aliens were discharged on the surety of two 'British subjects of good standing' and a monetary bond, but discharged on condition that they move away from their places of habitation, causing an influx of the displaced into London.

The races were difficult to categorise. Those from Alsace, for example, whose region seemed in permanent limbo between France and Germany. Officials added their views: 'A true Pole will be a friend, but Polish nationality might be claimed by mischief-makers,' the Police Commissioner Sir Edward Henry said.

The country became alive with spy fever, every rumour amplified by populist papers. German bakers were lacing London's bread with arsenic, reservoirs were being poisoned, gun caches were said to have been unearthed at German clubs, their barbers would cut Englishmen's throats, they lit fires to guide enemy Zeppelins in. (After the Great Fire of London – we were at war with the Dutch and rumour had it that enemy agents had started the fire – it is reported that Dutch and other foreigners who might have been Dutch were attacked and lynched in the streets.)

John Bull, whose editor Horatio Bottomley, MP for Hackney South was later imprisoned for fraud involving war bonds, led a campaign called the Anti-German Pledge, under which supporters pledged not to employ, buy from, or have social intercourse with anyone of German origin, and to ostracise from respectable company women who had married Germans. "A Million Members Wanted. Enrol at Once!" Women were called on to prove themselves by divorcing German spouses, and a special society formed to advise and help them. The Express demanded the sacking of all German hotel and restaurant employees

Firms checked the backgrounds and origins of their workforces and sacked if in doubt. Signs went up: "Germans need not apply", "No Germans served here". The families began by pawning or selling everything, then became destitute, sleeping in streets and parks and foraging. Their children were excluded from claiming school meals and medicines could not be bought for them. Organisations that helped, such as the Society of Friends (the Quakers) were known as 'Hun Coddlers', 'Friends of Fritz'.

The war didn't end in a few weeks as expected: it went badly. German forces swept through Belgium, Edith Cavell was executed for helping British prisoners escape. The Lusitania was sunk in 1915 and a medal struck in Germany to commemorate it. The U-boat blockade led to rations being reduced, Kitchener's ship H.M.S. Hampshire was torpedoed in 1916, conscription began for the first time, our troops gassed in the trenches. The Easter Rising took place in Dublin, a German cruiser bringing arms to the rebels was intercepted and scuttled by its crew.

Nights of rioting followed the sinking of the Lusitania, particularly in large cities such as Glasgow, Newcastle, Liverpool, Manchester, London, Southend and Cardiff. German shops and houses were looted for furniture and family belongings. Initially the targets were German, but the looting spread to shops in general. The campaign to intern enemy aliens hotted up: it was for their own safety. "The Germans have become a danger to the public welfare" said the Times – they were causing the people to riot. John Bull was less coy: "Exterminate every German-born man (God forgive the term!) in Britain". A Destitute Aliens Committee was formed, recommending mass rehousing on the Isle of Man, and internment began in earnest 'for their own safety and that of the community'.

The Trading with the Enemy Amendment Act 1916 forbade Germans to trade in the UK and wound up and confiscated their businesses. 'We must destroy every German business and get these businesses ourselves,' Sir Edward Carson MP and cabinet member urged.

My grandfather would have been thirty-seven in July 1915 when enemy aliens of fighting age were instructed to pack a few things in a case and report to their nearest police station. He had married my grandmother Florence Stonehewer, one of the Stonehewers of Love Lane (later Putney Bridge Road) Wandsworth, her father a builder and decorator, in 1908 and had two sons by the time of his internment, my father Jack Frederick (christened Friedrich) aged two, and uncle Mandy, or Ernest (christened Ernst) aged four. When asked what sort of things they should pack they were told to pack as if they were going on a short holiday. They were marched to yells of 'Huns!', 'Baby killers!' through the East End streets to Richie's jute factory, Carpenter's Road Stratford, which had been derelict for ten years. Roof panels were smashed and missing, the drainage backed up and flooded during rain; initially taps, lights, toilets didn't work, there were no baths or heating. Their cases were taken from them under the term 'luggage control', the contents scattered on the wet ground in a search for sharp objects and small tools; stamps and money taken. There were no chairs, or day rooms to withdraw to, the basic food was a stew of beef fat and offal. They scrubbed the guards' sleeping quarters on their knees while they smoked and looked on, the buckets used the same ones in which the stew was made. They slept on boards or directly on the ground.

A boy conscript in his teens, pissing and shitting himself as he goes over the top to his death, would have taken conditions like these, as would his family, given the choice. I can only tell my story, my family's story. It's a secondary one, painful in a smaller, different way.

So - the enemy aliens who had said probably cheerful goodbyes to their families and set off with small cases containing a few days of essentials in this way were held in unused and unusable buildings until a better option could be found. At Newbury the accommodation was horse boxes, without heat or light.

Alexandra Palace on Muswell Hill was London's pleasure hub. The central hall was ninety feet high, 130 yards long and 60 wide, with a dominant circular stained glass window and brightly coloured statues of town crests and royals from the time of William the Conqueror onward high along the side walls. A huge organ, the Wills organ, was its centrepiece. There was a main dining hall with a capacity of over a thousand, a banqueting hall, post and telegraph office, boating lakes, a monkey house, bandstand, Japanese, Moorish and Egyptian houses, an exhibition centre, circus ring for three thousand spectators, stabling for equestrian events and horse racing, a theatre. Boxing and wrestling events were held, fireworks displays, ballooning, cooking demonstrations, clay pipe making, sheepdog trials.

It was an unlucky place though. Gutted by fire in the late Eighteen-hundreds, it was reopened for the new millennium with the addition of a velodrome and skating rink using a polished marble floor. Two years on, two and a half thousand troops and two thousand horses occupied it for six months prior to the delayed coronation festival of Edward VII, and ruined the grounds. It was allowed to deteriorate and become overgrown, to the point where performers and audiences had to remain in their overcoats and gloves at concerts, because of unrepaired roof panels – a November 5th concert was disrupted as sparks from the fireworks came in through the holes. At another concert the organ gave up the ghost mid-performance. The circus ring fell into disuse and was broken up.

Its first wartime occupants were Belgian refugees, but by 1915 it was taken over for internees, housing three thousand at a time. Housing is a word, in this case referring to three thousand beds of straw sacking in line after line in an open hall whose closeness prevented inmates from moving without making contact with one another. Privacy of any kind was impossible, there were no tables, stools or boxes for possessions. Men who needed the toilet had to find five others before they would be marched through at bayonet point. Sudden noise affected particularly the older prisoners – at night sentries paced the sleeping areas heavily, it was said the dropping of a rifle would wake a thousand men. There were two long counts a day and three inspections a week. Tiny incidents would cause fights, small surprises such as the dropping of a plate or appearance of a cat would cause mass uproar. Rules were often deliberately broken in the hope of a punishment away from the main areas.

In time, jobs were allocated and rotated every six weeks to give men an occupation and the chance to earn a few shillings: jobs in the kitchens, stores, offices, toilets and washrooms, coal carrying, etcetera. Garden plots were given out; some firms in the area employed watchmakers for example, die-sinkers, gardeners, road menders (the government deducted their board from wages). So a small economy emerged and spaces began to be found for tailors to do repairs, woodworkers, who made picture frames, boxes for varied uses, toys, ornaments carved from wood and bone, but largely the work had to be done between beds. Small tools and materials were brought in by wives and family members, and by the Quakers. In winter the gas lighting was too dim for these activities and frustration levels would rise. Men would gaze at nothing for hours, play patience endlessly, gamble, small arguments becoming normal.

But improvised partitions between beds start appearing, in spite of the regulations, small cabinets and seats. The YMCA provided building materials for classrooms, which were constructed by inmates. Teachers among them offered lectures in sciences, languages, for example, history, literature, economics. There were now musical concerts, dramas, gymnastics, football matches. There were interruptions to progress though. New internees arrived at such a rate that the new rooms had to be filled with beds. As the final internment centre at Knockaloe, Isle of Man, was extended, groups were being regularly trans-ferred there and the courses would be disrupted or discontinued. In winter the rooms even when free were too cold, and classes in any case came to a close after the last count at 4 - 5pm. Food was scarce in the country and rations were reduced. At a place like Alexandra Palace where food was minimal and of poor quality - largely bread, salted herring, smelts, potatoes and other root veg, pulses - reductions led to under-nourishment and hospitalisations. Stomach ulcers and abdominal ruptures were common. Food parcels became rare and were often uneatable because of delays in delivery, in some cases the recipient given only the string and wrapping. Those that did get through would tend to be eaten furtively.

This to the accompaniment of a hostile campaign in the press: "Our well-fed and pampered Huns", "Get rid of the Huns but spare our dogs". As humiliations increase the internee's idealisation of his family increases, he spends hours grooming himself for visits, where a board is placed across the table to prevent contact, which the shorter ones aren't able to see over. Children not allowed to sit on their father's knee, or may no longer recognise him; and may be remote from the mother as well, who spends her days scavenging or working long hours off the records in a sweat shop. In the camp theatre there is a glut of produc-tions featuring scenarios of family misery in which the father is helpless and unable to give protection. Internees may hear of a death, eviction, the closure and confiscation of their business, pauperism, their children in a workhouse. Attendance at a funeral is subject to Home Office permis-sion, delays sometimes meaning it has already taken place when the permit arrives, or the internee isn't located in time, his documents lost in transit after confiscation, or scattered and left in the rain during initial luggage checks. The officials never fully aware of who they had in their custody. There is general mental deterioration, moodiness,

coarseness, organised activities shunned, replaced by list-
less groups standing around. Endless letters to the
authorities composed and recomposed, occasional
suicides.

*     *     *     *

Ernst's stay at Alexander Palace can't have been long,
records place him on the Isle of Man from August 14th
1915.

The transit and initial housing at Knockaloe is as bad.
Three hundred beds for four thousand prisoners, chronic
blanket shortage, no sheets; long roll calls in the open, i.e.
in the rain, watchtowers and floodlights, scarcity of doctors,
those available equipped with aspirin and a stethoscope.

But what's the point of repetition? Knockaloe operated
to a plan: finally there are 23,000 men in compounds of
one thousand, each compound comprising huts of thirty,
batched together in sixes, so batches of 180 men; the
compound divided into four sub-camps separated by
barbed wire – communication between sub-camps is
possible but requires a permit. In Douglas the holiday
camp is requisitioned for officers and gentlemen, they
receive an allowance of a pound per week and may have
their own tent or hut, with servants; they are entitled to an
alcohol quota of two bottles of beer or one bottle of wine a
day and can buy a breakfast of bacon, eggs and
marmalade.

But the main camp is my concern. In time there are
trestle tables and chairs, bed boards, mattresses, blankets,
latrines and wash houses. When essentials for survival are
in place, a society emerges. Camp captains are elected,
committees formed. Ernst is part of the kitchen committee,

a prestigious role – food and post are the focal points of every day. Rations are allocated to each compound, the committee is responsible for feeding a thousand men. Food is predominantly bread (ingredients for bread, they bake their own), some form of meat or fish, tea, coffee, salt, sugar, condensed milk, margarine, vegetables, oatmeal. Letters out are subject to an allocation – two letters a week of twenty-four lines max., they may only refer to private or business affairs and are subject to censorship; this is done in Liverpool, where there is a bottleneck of several weeks. The left-behind families move frequently, often furtively, and a letter will re-arrive at the camp weeks later marked 'Not known/Gone away'. With newspapers prohibited, rumours and anxiety increase.

In time, prisoners' aid organisations are given the right to give advice, help with letter writing and maintaining contact with families, tracing belongings, notification of funerals and hospitalisations

Parcels can be received, usually of food, cigarettes, money. Paid work is sometimes possible, making fishing nets, basket making on a commercial scale, furniture making, much of it for areas of newly-liberated France, pipe and brush making, mail bags; work outside the camp – agricultural, especially harvesting, land reclamation, mining and stone breaking, peat cutting, building a sewage system, canalisation, road and railway building and main-tenance, aerodrome building, thermometer making. An economy emerges, a camp bank, money lenders. Those lower down the food chain offer services to the privileged, as boot makers and repairers, tailors, furniture makers, gardeners, postmen, coal carriers, barbers, shoe-blacks, stewards, potato peelers. Food, tobacco, toiletries, medi-cines can be bought at the camp shop. Barter, gambling, forgery of money orders, card-sharping and theft complete the economy.

As the war becomes bogged down a sense of permanence takes hold. Camp place names emerge – Kaiser Wilhelm Strasse, Potsdamer Platz, Hotel Emden, Zeppelin Villa. Camp newspapers are created, initially wall newspapers, eventually printed off, some with runs of a thousand or more. Werden, Quousque Tanden, Lager Echo, die Hunnen. The Lager Zeitung ran twenty-six issues from mid-1916, average run two and a half thousand. With books, tools and equipment from the Red Cross, Prisoners' Relief Agency, Society of Friends, etc., libraries are established (Camp IV is said to have had a library of eighteen thousand books by the end of the war), art exhibitions, musical performances, horticultural shows, churches and bible classes appear, a high school for the young with certificates validated by the Prussian Ministry of Ed., scientific and literary societies, a university. Sport activities involve huge numbers, there are leagues established in all imaginable sports, even a three-hole golf course. A cinema is set up in 1917. Dramatic productions take place nightly – at one time or another there are twenty theatre companies in Knockaloe, involving as well as cast - stage hands, costume makers, scenery painters, electricians. There are extensive craft workshops, ornaments and trinkets produced from bones, corned beef tins, discarded fabric, whatever can be come by.

"Our well-fed and pampered Huns…" It's tempting. The flower of youth being gassed in Flanders. Ernst died more than a decade before I was born, so I'm free to indulge such thoughts without guilt if I wish to. But this is not exclusively his story, it is the story of the scraps, the leftovers: the Haydens' story. I fill in what gaps I can.

I would guess Ernst had a better interment than many. I've seen four photos of different kitchen committees, so four out of a possible twenty-three. By chance, the clearest shows my grandfather – there are ten men, mostly standing in working clothes; he is older than them (he would have been maybe 38), seated in a suit looking directly at the camera and my guess is he is the head chef. The role would take up most of his time, so his entire life in the camp would have been purposeful.

But it's not Centre Parks. These are men who have been severed from their families, who are safe in the broad meaning of the word while their families are vulnerable and unsafe in a climate that is hostile to them. "Now for the Vendetta!" a John Bull headline screams, "Vengeance is Mine, Saith the Lord!"; others: "Huns Are Well-fed in Prison Camps in England. Cakes, Music, Jam and Sausage"; "At Douglas the Teutons are like masters amongst us… They whistle and sing and march along the seafront and admire the beauty of the country." 'Hun wives' are given a subsistence allowance by the government but it is discretionary.

So, winding back to early 1915, my grandmother Florence Stonehewer has two boys aged under two and four, a German name and an imprisoned enemy alien for a husband. I knew her well, through my childhood, but her story was not for my young ears, probably not for anyone's ears. She moves frequently, and Anglisises her name from Kayser to Hayden. Decades later, I saw the signatures of my grandfather's adult siblings: as the family story began to come to light a mid-air revelation came to me, flying home from Stuttgart with an armful of copied archive material, and I pulled urgently at the arm of the woman in the next seat who was quietly minding her own business and reading a book. 'Look – look what I've found!' In some of the signatures, the swirling Old German characters appear to be other than what they are. The initial K is written with a horizontal joining the two parts, I-<. Add in the decorative swirl and you can see a copperplate H. The lower case s has a rising stem which resembles a d, and the final r ends with a flourish, becoming a partial underline, resembling an n. Hayden.

I imagine at some point before the war an official, a counter assistant at the Post Office maybe, has looked at a form carrying the signature and has addressed her mistakenly as Mrs Hayden. Saving her the trouble later of having to find herself an English name. The woman marked her place with a finger, showed an appropriate, brief, level of interest and continued reading.

*    *    *    *

Knockaloe is an exposed former farm, then territorial army base, near Peel. The climate for much of the year is windswept and rainswept. The huts are constructed of creosoted weatherboard, rain blows in through the gaps, inside walls are black with damp and mould, clothing and belongings become mildewed; prisoner numbers mean the outside is a swamp in wet weather. The allocation of sleeping space is six feet by four (a coffin is six by two). Inmates are never alone, never in mixed company, quietness can't be found.

Numbers of young internees are unable to speak or understand German, and have never been to Germany. Paranoia is rife, Schieberen, people who screw over others for advantage, are hated; small habits or incidents generate festering hatreds, meanness prevails, a coarse, bestial sense of humour. Men become despondent, don't shave, don't wash, don't dress. Factions form.

One of the most profound sources of tension is sexual. There are three very complete accounts of WW1 internment by internees themselves – one by Rudolf Rocker, one by A.L.Vischer, one by Cohen-Portheim; they all deal with the question of sexual frustration. Vischer, writing about Alexandra Palace says there are a large number of 'intimidation cases' and 'self pollution' leading to morbidity. Rocker's account is more detailed. He says "… the sufferer (of sexual suppression) will seek to overcome the desire out of himself, or he will seek satisfaction by violence or in other ways. With the men here interned (in Alexander Palace) only the former way is open, owing partly to the impossibility of doing otherwise… The effects of this sexual suppression are, however, everywhere to be seen and show themselves equally in the moodiness of the younger, idealistic or cultured men, as well as in the cynical remarks and jests of the sexual blasé… Cases of direct pathological perversion have been comparatively rare in this camp, though I believe this evil is much more widespread in the larger and more isolated camps."

Vischer refers to masturbation whereby men "try with all their might to keep the recollection of their womenfolk alive… Homosexual practices are probably not as frequent as may be imagined. Mutual abuse would be more likely to be indulged in" – (the distinction not made clear). Cohen-Portheim claims that sex between men in the camps was extremely rare because "the camp offered no possibility of isolation". Vischer says that instead "it is not uncommon for two friends to associate like lovers". This brings to mind a moving passage in Sebastian Barry's 'Days Without End' in which groups of gypsum miners in outback U.S.A. come into town to watch a dramatic entertainment performed by two men. The miners are essentially interned among fellow men for this period of their lives.

"Our dresser comes behind my screen and assists me in the dark challenge of my underwear. What goes on first, what is added like a riddle next. The stays and the corset and the bosom holder and the padded arse and the cotton packages for breasts. And the soft under-blouse and the petticoats and the dress itself as stiff as a coffin-board. The dress as yellow as water in moonlight. Rich stitching, brackets of lace, and tucks, and crosshatched sides. A fog of flower-printed muslin before and behind. All good in the light, we trust. Stagelight that will conspire with us, and make us into creatures not ourselves, wonders of people. Then the manager of the acts gives us the nod. We stand in the wings listening to the act that goes before us… I step on the stage and find the lights blazing against me and yet in the same instance pulling me forward. I am like something left over after a storm. Slight, a waif. It is like I am underwater in a pool of brightness. Slowly slowly I walk down towards the watching men. Something strange has happened, the hall has fallen into silence. Silence more speaking than any sound. I guess they don't know what they are seeing. I guess it is true that they are seeing a lovely woman. Soft-breasted woman, like something off a picture of such dames. Now there rampages through me a thrill such as might be got otherwise only from opium. I might be one of the footlights, with a burning wick for a heart. I don't utter a blessed word… John Cole all spit and polish approaches from the far side of the stage and we hear the men draw in their breath like a sea tide drawing back on the shingle of a beach. He approaches and approaches. They know I am a man because they have read it on the bill. But I am suspecting that every one of them would like to touch me and now John Cole is their ambassador of kisses. Slowly slowly he edges nearer. He reaches out a hand, so openly and plainly that I believe I am going to expire. The held-in breath of the audience is not let out again. Half a minute passes. It is unlikely any of them could of holded their breath like this underwater. They have found new size in their lungs. Down down we go under them waters of desire. Every last man, young and old, wants John Cole to touch my face, hold my narrow shoulders, put his mouth against my lips. Handsome John Cole, my beau. Our love in plain sight. Then the lungs of the audience giving out, and a rasping rush of sound. We have reached the very borderland of our act, the strange frontier... John Cole and myself break the spell. We part like dancers, we briefly go down to our patrons, we briefly bow, and then we have turned and are gone. As if for ever. They have seen something they don't understand and partly do, in the same breath. We have done something we don't understand neither and partly do... The crowd behind the curtains now are clapping, hooting, stamping. There is a craziness in it all that betokens a kind of delicious freedom. Notions are cast off. If only for a moment. They seen a flickering picture of beauty. All day they've laboured in the beds of gypsum crystals, hacking and gathering. Their fingernails are a queer white from the work. Their backs are sore and they must troop out again in the morning. But for a minute they loved a woman that ain't a real woman but that ain't the point. There was love in Mr Titus Noone's hall for a crazy foggy moment. There were love imperishable for a rushing moment."

$$* \qquad * \qquad * \qquad *$$

The protagonists can't replace sufficient boys to kill quickly enough and the war collapses to a close. The vendetta begins. Internees are deported to Germany leaving their torn families to look after themselves. Not permitted to return for ten years. They are shipped to the mainland and put on trains to Spalding and Boston, housed for days wherever, a workhouse for example, unheated, no canteen, no place for the luggage they have, then onto ships again for Rotterdam or the Hook. Searches more hostile this time, boxes and cases thrown into the water. The ships are overcrowded, there is sleeping on the decks. Baggage is searched during the crossing, books and papers destroyed, stolen.

In Rotterdam the holding stations are more humane – hospitals, convalescent homes; men are given flowers, chocolate, tobacco if lucky. Germany is devastated, there is mass unemployment and a revolutionary climate. Men are released by the agencies when they can give an address in Germany. Some can't – paperwork is lost or contacts broken. For many it's better to slip the authorities and remain in Holland. Ernst does this, and ends up some years later working as a chef on the passenger ship SS Bremen. When his wonderful and sad story (our wonderful and sad story) came to light, I met with the grandsons of one of his brothers, Julius Paul, who'd made it to America. The family story goes that whenever Ernst docked at Manhattan he would visit his nephew – Julius Paul's son - who had married an Italian, and bring a whole salami back from his travels, from her home region. Years later it transpired he'd been buying them from a deli in downtown New York.

I have a single photo of him in England sitting in an unkempt garden with two of his sons, my father and uncle. From their apparent ages one can guess it was taken in 1927-8, so it seems he returned, to London but not to my grandmother, and died in St Pancras hospital aged 55, in 1933.

## 10.  TELEFONICA (Minuet) - SPAIN

March 21 pm (log):

Arrive home to find one telegraph pole lying in the ditch in front of our house.  Celebrate by taking a photo of it with my new digital camera.  Reflect that when the pole is finally doing the job for which it was fashioned, I will be able to send its picture via the internet to friends all over the world.

March 31 8.15 am (log):

Driving down the hill towards Santa Cristina, about a mile from our home, I see an ancient flat-bed lorry parked on the other side of the road with three Men squashed side-by-side together in the cab, gazing at an unfolded map which covers most of the windscreen.  I slew to a halt about a hundred yards further on when it dawns on me that the long brown thing on the back looks like a telegraph pole.  With leaping heart I reverse backwards up the hill, stop alongside the lorry and lower the window.

Are you from Telefonica, by any chance?

The one nearest the door, gazing down at me from his elevated and airy seat, decides for reasons best known to himself that my question is not worth answering.  Instead, he counters with one of his own.  Or at least, he says something that I interpret as a question.  What he actually says is, "Avinguda Ridaura B43" in a voice caked with black tobacco smoke and marinated in cheap brandy.  But what do I care about that? I'm so happy I could cry.  "Follow me," I shout gaily.  Five minutes later we are outside my house.  While Rosa looks on happily I show them the other telegraph pole lying in the ditch. "That came a week ago," I say.  "Other blokes, I should think." The leader of this unit looks at me with open contempt and says something in a language I don't recognise. "I'll leave you to it then," I say. I beam at Rosa, give her surreptitious thumbs up, and drive off.

March 31 12.15 pm (log):

Return to find two telegraph poles fully erect. I admire the way they taper gracefully skywards and think for a moment how nice Union Jacks would look fluttering from their tops. What a bizarre and ridiculous notion. Perhaps I am not well. Cannot understand why the original compact little unit of three Telefonica operatives and their lorry has now been joined by a Telefonica van and two Aqualia lorries. Six Men are sitting on the flat-bed eating sandwiches, two are chatting by the pole furthest from our house, and another two are poking around at the base of the other pole with some kind of long-handled garden tool. "What's going on?" I ask the nearest Man. He looks at me as if I'm something he's been given to eat that he doesn't like the look of and mutters a few words in that language I don't recognise. "You missed the excitement," says Rosa, emerging from our house. "They hit the mains. The water was this high." She holds up her hand about a foot above her head.

# 11. TOWN TWINNING

In 2006 the Observer printed a little filler:

"JUST CAN'T TWIN

Pity Manteo, North Carolina. It thought it was twinned with Bideford in Devon. But when David Riley, a Manteo goodwill ambassador, crossed the Atlantic for a visit bearing a commemorative clock and mugs in tribute, he was rebuffed. Manteo's place had been usurped by Landivisiau in Brittany. Bidefordites claimed no knowledge of their long-lost sibling over the water. But according to Manteo's records, as recently as 1984, 15 of the town's citizens - 1.4% of its entire population - visited Devon to celebrate the union. Town-twinning is a tired old institution that might be livened up by a dose of competition. So we recommend that Mr Riley offer his clock and mugs to Landivisiau in a bid to poach the twin town from the perfidious Bideford."

Sometimes a really good idea can seem outdated and risible. The trouble with a lot of good community ideas is when the initial euphoria dies away they get bogged down with structure, hierarchy and regulations. Our town is in Worcs and has a fairly standard twinning with two towns, one in France, one in Germany. I had nothing to do with it other than being a member with my wife who was on the committee, and tagging along for the occasional exchange. One night she came back from a meeting and informed me that I was Germany. I opened one eye. As in German visit liaison person, she said - I'd been co-opted.

I didn't have a clue how things operated, and decided to invite myself to a gathering of other Worcestershire twin towns to see if I could pick up any tips. These were monthly meetings which we were always invited to but never went. I found it interesting. They were all struggling with dwindling memberships, and trying to figure out startling new initiatives to reverse this. A popular strategy seemed to be to instigate another twinning with a new country. Worcester were the go-to for this, they were like players in the dating scene, on Tinder the whole time. During my seven years as Germany, in addition to their traditional partnerships in Germany and France they also had an association with Worcester, Mass., and put out feelers for new liaisons with towns in Spain, Lithuania, Gambia, Italy, China, Kashmir, and - wait for it - Gaza. The Gaza thing was unfairly exploited by the local paper: they made a headline of it following a bit of informal pub talk, and when their delegates walked in late for the next joint meeting we all ducked under the tables.

Fair play to them, they wanted their exchanges to be relevant. But leaving aside the cheap jokes about Gaza - who can go to these places that always seem to be further and further off? Only the well-off and retired. And so, instead of revitalising the thing they want to save, initiatives like this tend to slowly kill it.

Over a period of time I picked up a lot of small, fun ideas from these joint meetings. Simple things work. Redditch held an annual boules tournament with their French town, and one year the guys from a separate Tanzanian twinning group that had formed from students of Birmingham Uni and Selly Oak College were invited along to see how things were done. They won it. There was a similar quaint story from the chap from Kidderminster, who are twinned with Husum in the far north of Germany, about thirty miles from the Danish border. Husum had a cricket team apparently, and in the early days the Kiddy guys thought it would be amusing to bring some cricketers over and show them how the game is really played. They weren't aware that Husum plays in the first division of the Danish league, and were given a comprehensive beating. There was a detail that intrigued me: that beyond the outfield, Husum's ground is ringed with little chalets, because most of the Danish teams who play them have too far to travel to get back the same day, so the players overnight in the chalets. I imagine Husum away might be regarded as a peach of a fixture.

Ridiculously simple things like beetle drives, skittle nights, bingo can spring to life in the hands of groups from different cultures determined to have fun. From bingo, by the way, I learned the French for two fat ladies: la double globule.

The twin-town forum ran occasional events as a kind of bonding thing. One was the annual quiz, hosted by a different town each year. Normally things were close, but one of the years when our town was hosting a team won with ease. Actually, we thought we'd been in with a chance when we were given a spare kid who didn't seem to have any owners. He sat tight-lipped colouring in a Man. United badge for most of the night, till 'Which is the smallest Tele-Tubby?' came up. 'Tinkie Winkie,' he muttered in a Pavlovian response, not even raising his head. We scribbled it down, making a phalanx over our paper so the other teams wouldn't see we were writing a long rather than short word. Answer: Po. We called them up to the stage and presented them with the trophy.

'Congratulations. Which twinning association are you with?'
'Don't know mate, we just heard there was a quiz…'
'Well where are you from?'

'Ombersley.'

'Ombersley doesn't have a twinning association.'

'What's twinning?'

We went over to the Droitwich lot.

'Ombersley's nearest you, congratulations you've won the trophy, take it.'

'We don't want it.'

'Nor do we. Here - it's yours.'

Some twinnings have huge incompatibilities, and you wonder how they ever got off the ground in the first place. Our town is twinned with a French coastal town in Picardy whose tiny population almost disappears in the winter and quintuples in summer. The friendship survives, and thrives, for the simple reason that the town of Bewdley is special to them. De Gaulle was permitted to gather and billet his Free French cadets in a country mansion about a mile from where I'm sitting, and in 1941 five of their teenaged boys put to sea in an open boat to join him, and made it across to Eastbourne two days later. They were presented to Churchill, and transported to Bewdley to prepare alongside their compatriots to retake their country. Relations with the current occupants of the estate had been fractious for years, but eventually a tentative rapport was established and the French party were offered a visit to the house itself. To their and our surprise, the owner greeted them in a sash of the Free French and brought out various bits of memorabilia that had been found over the years, including some handwritten letters, and this brought a number of their group to tears.

As a digression - in our town visitors' book which anyone can handle and write in, one of the early pages contains a signed note from de Gaulle, just sitting alongside the rest.

The difficulty with our German exchange was transport. Birmingham airport is close to us, but to get there by air involved flying to places like Hannover, Erfurt, Dusseldorf or Frankfurt, all a couple of hours away. I wasn't a very imaginative travel organiser: we had stop-off time in Brussels (via Eurostar) and Hannover, but missed out on the beautiful centres of Erfurt and Dusseldorf. The Germans were more resourceful and would actually choose to travel somewhere further afield and take in, say, York or Manchester. One year they flew to Manchester and I said, OK, which city - Manchester or Liverpool? They chose Liverpool, so we met them with a coach and took them for a day round the galleries, cathedrals, and so on. I thought the highlight would be the Beatles Museum because there were a few teens among the two groups, but that was only popular with my age group, it meant nothing to the kids, they went off to Anfield. Old gits trying to second-guess the young…

What's going on out there? Are committees always stacked with the old because the young are too busy with raising their kids and getting the mortgage paid, or is there a sea-change? No organisations as such in a few years, just spontaneous crowd events posted on the internet? I haven't got a clue - just know that silver haired committees tend to preoccupy themselves with trivia while the overall project runs into the sand, and in the case of town part-nerships, silver committees perpetuate the notion that twinning is a private affair for people who want to remember the war.

Having said that, we had some brilliant older members. On one exchange, we'd had a free day where the hosts decide what to do with their guests, and we were chatting at the evening do.

'Alright Dennis? Do anything interesting today?'
'Yes - went up in a glider.'

He was eighty. Another of our vets was interviewed for the newsletter. At the end of the interview he said, 'Most of this is true, but I've embroidered a little here and there.' It was full of daft recollections such as, 'Four of us were accommodated with the same host and we often had boiled eggs for breakfast, but there were four eggcups and only three eggs so we had to rotate. I thought this quite strange as there were at least twelve hens in the garden, perhaps only three were in lay...' When asked what his ambition was he said, 'I want to die when I'm ninety, shot by a jealous husband - I don't mind which one.' He made it to 84, and missed the shooting.

The arch rogue was Bob Dunn, a wonderfully vain and dandyish Scot in his late eighties. He wouldn't be inter-viewed, but as I was going called out, 'I got the D.S.O.' I turned round. 'Dick Shot Off - put that down if you want.' Bob was nearly blind, but had an eye for a looker wherever he was. At one time a stunning girl was struggling to do the clasp on a belt which she'd slipped back round her very slim waist at the airport security check and from a good twenty yards he clocked her and was there, ignoring his own shoes and belt: 'CAN I HELP YOU M'DEAR...' Under her beautiful ebony skin there appears an unmis-takeable bright red blush.

I was a few places behind him at a Dutch service station checkout. The till girl stopped and in very emphatic English said, 'Thank you. I will be sleeping by my self tonight.' A womaniser and rogue was what Bob wanted to be, and probably had been. He had a collection of ladies in pleasant cities of Europe who he would stay with in some kind of sequence. Along with his passionate eye for beauty, which he never stopped believing was reciprocated, he had an insatiable ear for language. We had a bi-lingual member who gave French classes in the back room of one of the town pubs. Her teaching style was traditional: we spent several weeks studying 'Le Petit Prince', which he'd sabotage by asking randomly, during a reading, whether a phrase of argot he'd picked up years earlier was still in use, or would she mind updating him. But on another occasion when I had to drop in about something, I found him listening to Arabic language lessons. He said he fancied going to Marrakesh later in the year.

I didn't always get on with Bob. In the early days when I'd been trying to organise my first exchange, there'd been a complication over his passport. We were on the phone - I hadn't met him face to face and may have used a slightly patronising tone. 'Och - go and stick your trip up your arse.' Brrrr... That was that. But as sometimes happens with a shaky start, things get better.

None of the above-mentioned are still with us, but they were an inspiration - their gratitude for and appetite for life is something I don't ever want to lose sight of.

There were wonderful oldies from our partner towns too. In 2009 we organised a Euro weekend in our town. Initially we'd thought it might be difficult to persuade shops to play ball, but over forty put out the flags and bunting and took part. It extended to pubs, estate agents, betting shops and funeral directors - obviously house sales weren't going to be conducted in euros but it looked good on the display. It caught the attention of Central News, who brought a crew down to do some interviews. One of our lovely aged guests who'd been involved for decades gave an interview full of loving emotion. 'When I come to Bewdley I'm always coming to my second home,' she said. Everyone got to a tele in time to watch, but saw only live football. A Manchester United - Everton cup game had run to extra time and the item was chopped.

I didn't join the twinning to talk about war specifically, or avoid talking about it. One of their visits coincided with some anniversary or other when we were glorifying our victory, and I asked our guests whether they felt they would like to discuss their war experiences, or not. They did, and it went ahead.

One of our guys kicked off with a lovely story about his father, who'd worked in a flat-roofed ammunitions, or maybe aircraft parts factory. They had the roof painted bright green, and his father's first job every morning was to go up and reposition the plastic cows, so the bombers wouldn't realise they were fakes.

But Kassel is not far from the old border with East Germany, and our visitors' experiences were bleak. Not one of them had a past untouched by war: a woman in her eighties as a child lost eleven members of her family from one direct hit on her house and the house next door, an event she couldn't tell of three-quarters of a century later without crying; the mother of one was taken every morning and raped by soldiers throughout the day, then returned to her children in the evenings; she also couldn't tell this without welling up with sadness, and possibly with guilt; there was a man whose father, after Germany was partitioned, cycled to the border approximately once every two years so his activities wouldn't be noticed, each time taking one child across in the dead of night to leave with relatives in the west – after the last one he was able to get his wife out, but the oldest had been so long without her he didn't recognise her. The oldest was the friend who told the story.

Finally, and poignantly, he set off to cycle the entire way to our town and back himself for one visit, a round journey of well over a thousand miles.

We would probably have been better advised not to hold a meeting of this type without a skilled counsellor present, but we did, and with a lot of goodwill and sympathy we got lucky. I think it was cathartic for our guests, who for maybe the first time were able to sit in the heart of a British town and say, 'You did this to us.'

One of our members ran a pottery studio in the town, and one of her very popular activities involved decorating mugs and plates, and having them fired in the same session. It was great for kids' parties and I think she had a hen party or two. So we incorporated this into a visit. We had to pair off, not with our own guests but randomly, ask each other questions about themselves, and decorate a mug in a way that reflected what they'd told us. My partner was the director of a language school, but nevertheless very introverted, and as we talked she came out of herself and we developed a rapport. I still have the mug she created, and she has mine. So we continued the conversations we had initiated, over the weekend, and she got the lowdown on the weekly German conversation class I attended. I told her that although my general vocabulary was poor, I had enough words on medical conditions to sit a nursing exam - the reason for this was, we were all of an age, and for the opening 'what I've been doing since last time' exercise, most of them would start with, 'Ich war im Krankenhaus mit mein Mann…'

She said that as long as she could fill her quota for the immigrant basic German courses the following year, she could slip me into one if I liked. I liked very much, and the next year I arranged the travel for the group, handed it over to one of the regulars, and set off for Kassel a fortnight early. Our usual exchange partners would have happily put me up, but they have impeccable English and that wasn't what I wanted, so I invited myself to stay with a lovely couple - he was an assembly line worker at the huge VW plant in Baunatal - who spoke no English at all.

I was nervous about doing the course, but it was one of the funniest experiences I've had in my life. In the class I was with immigrants from Russia, Kosovo, Kazakhstan, Egypt, Algeria, Poland, Angola, France and the U.S. - all needing to pass to gain the right to work, except the last two who were married to Germans and wanted to integrate better. To sit the exam they had to do I believe three hundred hours of language, culture and history classes. Every session, several would arrive late or go early because they were working off the books, mainly night shifts on the taxis, in hotels, etc.

A lot had children, and would just get up, gather their things and walk out muttering something like, 'Kid's got dentist..' The teacher would raise her eyebrows and carry on. One of the Angolans would jump up and down randomly when he felt the need to, usually when there were written exercises to do, and start dancing on the spot. I was in the place next to him one day when this happened, and after he'd done his thing we started to work together on the exercise. He had good street German, but it was clear not that he couldn't write German, but that he couldn't write. After that we worked together quite often, I was basically his scribe. He clearly wouldn't pass the test, this was an unfortunate flaw in the system. At the end of the fortnight he fist pumped me and said, 'You white Nigga man.' A cherished compliment.

As an aside: people often say German's a hard language to learn. I don't really get this concept that languages are harder or easier; if a child can learn from babyhood, the language must be learn-able. Though yes, harder if there are no connections at all to our own language. I get, for example that some south-east Asian languages are tonal. Some friends of ours have a grand-daughter, Maisie, and we were with them when their parents decided to take them to a maize maze. The mother said, 'Want to go to the maize maze Maise?' I guess that's what tonal languages are about. But the main romantic and germanic languages have a lot of carry over into English. I love the logicality of German. They're surprised when I say that, and the example I always give is 'die Amarmung' - a hug, or literally, an armarounding. I had difficulty getting my head round the simple verb, to remember: erinnern, until I realised it means innering, taking into oneself.

On one day we were asked to write a few sentences about ourselves and read them to the group. By then we knew a bit about each other so for amusement I wrote that I was born on February 30th, was given an elephant for my fifth birthday present, married the first of my six wives when I was thirteen, outlived my alter-ego who died two years ago; when I paid him a visit in heaven I also met Einstein, Idi Amin and Lenin. There were two Russians who always sat together, they were often late and very hungover, and would slump their heads on the desk for the first quarter-hour and sleep. They participated in the exercise though, they were awake by then. After I read mine out one of them looked ahead with a furrowed brow for a while. He leaned across his mate to check my writing. 'Hey,' he said, looking up. 'You… Thirty February. There is no thirty February.'

So vielen Danke Martina. That's how it works when things go well: your exchange partners might become lifelong friends, you include each other in the big parties, kids' weddings, anniversaries; you holiday with each other. Our continent becomes smaller and more closely-knit. Someone explain to me how this is not a good thing.

*      *      *      *

All small clubs and associations seem to be preoccupied with funding, twinning included. Funds for what, you might ask, and for twinning it seems that generally they're for the big unwanted gifts that get exchanged, or to subsidise a formal dinner evening with pompous over-the-top speeches. More enlightened groups might use funding to subsidise the young, or young families who otherwise wouldn't be able to join in with exchanges.

At our town's annual Christmas Lights festival, we had a tradition of offering soup to the punters. One of the first newsletters I ever read had this classic item: 'The Christmas Lights stall was a success. It didn't make money, but the objective of generating interest was achieved, and we had a chance to chat to people and about forty newsletters were given out. Sue, Anne and Julie were thanked for their work in organising.'

I offered to take it on. Aldi sold Glühwein quite cheaply, and we cleaned them out as soon as it appeared and did tea and coffee, hot chocolate, Glühwein with brandy and Glühwein without, and we cleared a bit over two hundred pounds. Basically, we just had a trestle table with access to power, a mulled wine urn on one side and a hot water urn on the other. The gang who'd looked after the stall said it had been too complicated - people would come up and ask for tea with sugar and not too much milk, coffee without sugar or milk, hot chocolate for the kids, a

Glühwein with brandy and another without. They were crossing over each other, spilling drink, getting different prices mixed up...

We knocked out the tea and hot chocolate and takings went up. A couple of years later, there was a serious miscarriage. We ran out of the Tesco and Co-op own-brand brandy we were using, just as trade was at its busiest. One of the women serving said there was a full bottle in their house, they didn't drink it. They lived nearby and she dashed off and fetched it. By now we had a row of Glühwein waiting to be topped up and a restless crowd. I whipped the top off and poured, and that kept us going a bit longer. After the night was done, I fancied a look through the bottles to see what she'd brought. It was a bottle of vintage cognac from her mother's cupboard - so our drunk punters had been treated to vintage tipple mixed into mulled wine. Ferguson - you total and complete WOMAN. What were you thinking??

That year we made £400 - we even sold tots of brandy to people who'd bought their mulled wine from other stalls.

Then things turned serious. We'd visited the Cologne christmas markets that year and I'd brought home a pack of Glühwein spices. It was a decorative box with muslin sachets in. I went over the ingredients and realised they were all spices we had, mainly for curries. I thought we could save money by making our own for the next year's stall, but the best you could do wine-wise was a litre wax carton of cooking wine for a fiver. However.. On our summer séjour in France I came across five-litre plastic barrels of basic table red for five euros. We got about twenty and housed them in the broom cupboard. In early December I cleared the kitchen and began industrial Glühwein production. It took some tweaking, but after a couple of hours of adjusting and sampling I was pissed but utterly content. The stuff was rocket fuel.

The biggest pan we had would do ten litres, so I did this several times over, decanting it into a beer brewing bin to cool then returning it to the barrels for storage. The kitchen was like a scene of blunt force murder, but the drink, at about 15%, was nectar. There was more of it than the barrels could hold because of additional ingredients, so we kicked off a week before the festival with a house party - tenner in for funds, drink all you want.

That year we made £560 and shifted the full hundred litres. The day started slowly. At one point our local under-taker passed. I called her back - she's a bit of a town character, she'd lent us the table we were using, I don't know if it was one they laid the stiffs out on. 'Try some..'; 'Oo no, I never drink this early..'; 'It's a sample, have a try.' She got halfway down and wheeled off along the quay shouting, 'This is wonderful'. That set the tone for the day. We accumulated a group of regulars who simply wouldn't go away, they stood there doing massive rounds and blocking the street. I was doing a fair bit of sampling to encourage the punters, not realising the stall hands had been marking my card. They did me for twenty at the end.

I didn't know it, but the next year would be our last. I'd given other members orders to bring home wine from their holidays, and brewed up 140 litres. My mission was to clear a grand. We did straight wine with brandy, nothing else except for the last batch which we did without for some reason, and set the price so there would be a minimum of messing with change. On a freezing day, our regulars found us early, they needed warmth and we gave it to them. They stood round tucking each new polystyrene cup into the last one until they were drinking from small towers. Their presence drew in other people who would have a snifter. 'Fuck - what is this stuff?' They'd down it and order up the next one. By the end I was superfluous. There was no point shouting to passers-by, the stall was so rammed there were no passers-by. As the time came round to close down I spotted one of our guys outside the pub over the road having a quiet puff and a Hobson's. 'Stand's closing mate, you'd better be quick.' He emptied the pub and they saw off the last urn. All that was left was the stuff without brandy which we hadn't bothered to heat up. A friend of ours farms just out of the town and had set up a sterilised apple juicing and bottling unit, and with his help we got seventy bottles from that, the last few from the brandied batches.

It was January before the first one exploded. Just sitting in a warm drinks cupboard, and - WOOF. When we were told I talked to my friend and he said there are two grades of bottle glass, one for still and one for gaseous. He only used still, and the wine had obviously continued fermenting in the bottles. I had about forty urgent calls to make as well as a bit of detection to figure out who'd bought it all. My sister and brother-in-law for a start, they live in Worthing and had taken some back.

'Hello?'
'Pete, great, how's it going?'
'Have you drunk the spiced wine?'
'Only two, we're…'
'Where are the others?'
'On the sideboard I think. Bob, can you see if…'
'Take them outside now.'

Another chap was local, fortunately a friend.

'Neville - the wine. Has any of it exploded?'
'Only one…'

It had splattered his kitchen walls. I grovelled and offered to redecorate.

'No, really, I've been meaning to get round to it. You've done me a favour.'

Gradually the danger passed and people either drank or disposed of it. Ironically, none of the brandied bottles burst, brandy suppresses fermentation apparently. And thanks to people's generous refusal to take refunds, we made the full grand.

That was our final year, I never did it again. Not because of the exploding bottles however - it was because we'd moved house and had the kitchen decorated, and there could be no argument with that. I've sat on the recipe for ten years and not told a soul, in spite of being asked a number of times, and now, finally, I'd like to share it in thanks for your kind readership.

This is what I wrote down for ten litres, you'll have to scale down for less. Or you could bottle it. Keep it in a fridge, preferably in the garage.

6.5 litres red wine
50cl ginger wine
25cl prune juice*
1 litre brandy
75cl any fruit juice
10cl vanilla essence
1.5 cups sugar
1 orange chopped into small pieces
(*prune juice is a key ingredient - used to be sold in the Co-op, or get cans of prunes and drain the syrup)

The spices are put on squares of muslin and tied into pouches:

2 teasp whole mixed spice
4 cloves
2-3" cinnamon stick
0.5 star anis
1cm vanilla pod
1 teasp coriander seed
4 - 5 whole peppercorns
3 whole cardamoms, split.

Use slow heat, don't boil. Squeeze spice pouch as you remove it.

© P.H. Cheers. Or as the Hungarians say: Egészségedre. Go easy, it's addictive…

*       *       *       *

There was actually a pot of funding administered by the EU, but it seemed like the pot of gold at the end of the rainbow, it eluded everyone. Except the guy from Redditch, who'd managed to tap it twice over the years. I asked him how, and he gave me a one-to-one seminar. Most of the money went to start-up twinning from the new eastern bloc EU countries, fair enough, but if you could show them a visit programme that involved broadly political initiatives - environmental, for example, or minority group inclusion - you might get lucky. Most groups couldn't be bothered with that, they just wanted trips to local beauty spots and dinner evenings. But Redditch found that if they incorporated a visit to, say, a recycling plant or water purification place, they could tick a few boxes. It was only an afternoon, no-one seemed to mind, and a couple of times they got lucky.

It occurs to me I might have maligned several of the Worcestershire twin towns so far in this piece. Don't make personal representations to me folks, all grievances should be taken up directly with the publisher…

I liked the idea of a political approach, and set up visits with talks and discussion to the Central Mosque Birmingham and the Welsh Parliament in Cardiff. We got lucky with the funding and lucky with the visits. They were both brilliant: our guide and tutor in Cardiff was Lorraine Barrett MS, who led a discussion on Welsh devolution alluding to the integration of East Germany for our guests; my memory of Central Mosque is the talk we were given on Islam was very clear and specific - my German isn't brilliant, but I distinctly heard my counterpart riffing on various religious views of her own in her translation to their group.

On the subject of funding, and outgoings - formal gifts as mentioned were always a bit of a ball-ache. No end of etched plates and plaques went in both directions, no-one ever knew what to do with them. The way over-the-top gifts that were exchanged in the first euphoric years of the partnership were equally useless but more memorable. One was a telephone kiosk, which I was told had pride of place in their town park until youths had shamefully smashed all the windows. I said, no - really - that's what you do with phone boxes.. Another was a pillar box. They took it on the coach and it was housed with one of the hosts and touched up in Royal Mail red before the ceremonial handover. It was wheeled down the roads on a sack trolley but got stuck in the mud, and they staggered onto the platform with it halfway through the main course. At the handover, the burgermeister posted a large letter of thanks and then took the key to open it up and hand the letter to our chairman. But the touch-up job had sealed the door shut and it took several minutes and a couple of bent dinner knifes to get it open.

What did Macmillan say: 'Events, dear boy. Events.' A visit that coincided with a decent event was always a potential winner. One of ours came on the weekend of the royal wedding (can't remember which one - William & Kate?) and the Upton-on-Severn Folk Festival. We kicked off with a day-long pub crawl for those who weren't watching the ceremonials with their hosts, finishing with a balti, thereby achieving my long-term goal to drive the exchanges downmarket. The folk festival I'd never been to and hadn't heard of anyone who had, but it sounded like a promising day out. So the following day, before we left the coach I explained there'd be street music and some dancing - other than that I had no idea. The place was theirs to explore, see you back here 6pm.

It was nuts. There were small stages dotted about the town, but the weirdest I think they're called troupes would simply find a street corner and start dancing. There were scores of them, from all over the country, blacked-up faces, crows' beaks and feathers, flowers, branches and bowls of fruit on their heads, sticks, clogs, bells… one lot in drag, pink tutus and fishnet tights, with scarlet lipstick, heavily mascara'd eyes and wigs. And folk fans everywhere wearing waistcoats covered in badges from similar festivals all over Britain. It was wild. As we were walking back to the coach I fell in step with one of the visitors. 'What did you think?' I asked her. 'Oh it was wonderful, so typically English.' I said was it fuck, I'd never seen anything like it in my life.

Another visit coincided with Ladies' Day at Worcester Races. Everyone got up really smart and we loaded the picnic hampers, not Fortnum & Mason but fairly good, with champers flutes and everything, and set up among various other brilliantly dressed parties doing the same thing.

Several stag and hen parties, all looking great until about five in the afternoon when they started falling off their stools, knickers in the air. Oh it was wonderful, so typically English…

An absolutely integral part of twinning exchanges is reckoned to be the home-stay. You say with a family, not in a hotel or hostel talking English all weekend with your English friends - you immerse yourself in the culture. In theory. But what happens if you're mis-matched, your host is a chain smoker or has rotweilers, or rabid political views? In that case the host won't come on the return visit, and the guest won't offer to host anyway, so they'll both be lost for good. Or families with two or three kids, how can they reciprocate with maybe three bedrooms max, even if they could afford the trip to start with. Also - couples who had made good connections from the outset weren't going to give each other up, why should they? So the most hospitable, easy-going people were always taken. One year before my time the committee decided to break up established pairings, so everyone would have the same chance of a drawing a decent family. So the people who stood to be detached from long-standing host-partnerships simply left the twinning and continued to stay with each other informally. I came to the conclusion that staying in a hotel or hostel was OK, and as relationships formed, invitations to stay would probably follow.

My wife and I had the daft experience of joining a second twinning group for a while, this one in Brittany where we had our shared house. We used to park at Hofgeismar Platz in Pont Aven, and I thought, I know that name… It's a town very near our own twin-town, pretty, with half-timbered buildings in the centre, a friend we knew worked at the college. It was their twin-town. Wonder how you join, I thought. Not the way you join Bewdley Twinning it turned out: twenty quid thanks, sign here, how big's your house? For Pont Aven Jumelage you had to make an appointment with the mayor, get powdered up and appear at the due time. The mayor posed questions in slow deliberate French, gave our tentatively phrased answers careful scrutiny, and after deliberation showed us to the door. We received a letter of acceptance bearing the mayoral seal a few days later.

The twinning is heroic - it's a complete mis-match in a number of ways. Neither town being connected to the other by air, the established way of travel is eighteen hours non-stop on a coach, arrive shattered, weekend with hosts, back on the coach for eighteen hours, home. Apart from one local lady who's married to a German there is virtually no language mutuality at all, so most communication is done with hand gestures with the occasional one-syllable noun. There's a lot of fatigue. Our guests expressed puzzlement tinged with a bit of disappointment that they'd drawn the English holiday-makers, not a vrais, sorry, echte, French couple. That is until they experienced the Sunday Full English. We call them down and get ready to dig in. 'No - wait! Kamera!' They run back up for it and take photos from every angle before we can start.

I was game to do the round trip on the coach the following year, thought thirty-six hours bonding with our Breton neighbours would be fascinating, but was finally dissuaded. It's not an exchange for the faint-hearted.

During my time as liaison, a very good exchange had developed between the two tennis clubs. Few members of either club knew or cared about twinning, they just wanted to play a few sets, have a good time, chill together. Since the team captains of both clubs were good friends I decided to help facilitate that exchange, which seemed more genuine, instead. The liaison person in Germany I'd worked with for seven years was tireless, but had the non-negotiable idea that a visit itinerary was a gift that would not be presented until the first gathering, when it was expected to be received with cries of delight. From the members of both towns. This peeved me because I wanted the visit agendas to be a collective thing, but it peeved her fellow-members a whole lot more. I actually had a phone conversation with the friends we would be staying with - their call: they were exasperated that they simply couldn't give us an idea of what we'd be doing. I said, do you know Ehrenfried? No.. OK, leave it with me.. Ehrenfried I knew had just been co-opted onto the committee. I phoned him and asked what he knew about the itinerary. 'I shouldn't really tell you, but…' We phoned our friends back and gave them the agenda, which they passed on to the rest.

So I got involved with the tennis clubs instead. They are both very similar - relaxed, inclusive, involved in number of leagues but very social. It works well when you have a joint activity to hang the visits on. There are no speeches as such, just, Hi, great to see you again. I embellished mine with a joke once. It's a milestone when you can do a joke in another language, admittedly I was coached intensively by our host: A chap goes to the doctor with a worrying speech impediment - his voice has become very slurred and guttural, he can hardly make himself understood. The doc tells him to strip off behind the screen and takes a look. 'Well I can see the problem,' he says, 'you're enormous - it's dragging all your organs downwards, as far as your tongue.' The guy's distraught. The doc tells him the only thing would be to have a full transplant of the privates, but the procedure's still in the experimental stage, he'd have to sign a disclaimer, and they'd need him to agree to donate his own to help others who might be in difficulty. 'No problem,' the guy says ('nmyo pmwblem'), and signs the papers.

Some time after the op. he goes back for a debrief. He's delighted with his new voice, everyone can understand him, but the sex is crap. He says no matter what the risk, he'd like the procedure to be reversed. The doc sighs and says, 'I'wm afrwowd that's nwyt pwossubwl..'

The guys from Rot-Weiss Tennis Club tell me they still greet each other in this voice and crack up laughing.

## 12. AVA GARDNER - SPAIN

HERE ARE TEN THINGS I think you should know about Catalunya, some of them admittedly pretty inconsequential, but don't think any the worse of them for that:

1    If you'd googled Catalonia at midday on May 1 2006 you'd have come up with a respectable 61,100,000 results in 0.40 seconds.

2    According to Wikipedia, the total number of Catalan speakers in Spain, France, Andorra and Italy is more than 7.5 million.  Ten and a half million people are thought to speak or understand the language.

3    The public use of Catalan was banned by Franco after the Spanish Civil War.

4    Two hundred years odd before the Battle of Hastings, Charles the Bald, one of Charlemagne's grandsons, made local big-knob Wilfred the Hairy a Count. When Charles died a few years later, Wilfred the Hairy became Count of Barcelona and shortly after that Count of Girona as well, which marked the beginning of Catalunya as a place.  Not a country, mark you.  Countries didn't exist in those days, did they?  Catalunya was the southern flank of the Carolingian Empire and therefore a March. (Consider this history lesson a gift.  I'm not one hundred per cent satisfied with it, but it's my first attempt and I might get better.  Any merit it has should be attributed to Mr Derek Pitt, late of St Johns School, Leatherhead.)

5    If you find a Catalan girlfriend and get taken home to have dinner with her family, don't be surprised if your girlfriend's father calls you a cunt in Spanish (coño) at some point during the meal.  He's trying to put you at your ease.

6    If he calls you a cunt again when the Cava makes an appearance with the desert, you can finally lower your guard. You're one of the family now. On balance, however, and certainly if your language skills are not up to scratch, it's probably better if you don't risk returning the compliment. It's not what you say, you see, but the way you say it.

7    Leon Trotsky's assassin was a Catalan born in Barcelona called Ramon Mercader, who got at Trotsky by pretending to be a Belgian sports journalist and seducing his secretary. After the assassination, in Trotsky's fortified house on the outskirts of Mexico City, Mercader was detained, tried, and spent 20 years in a Mexican prison. He was released in 1960, went to Cuba, then on to the USSR, where he was decorated as a hero of the Soviet Union. In the mid-seventies he returned to Cuba and died there in 1978. His Mexican widow took his remains back to Russia, where today they lie in Kuntsevo Cemetery. All of this you can discover on the internet. Alternatively, you could visit the house and see for yourself where it all happened.

8    Ava Gardner had an affair with a Catalan bullfighter and actor while she was staying at a five-star hotel in S'Agaro, near where I live, making a film called Pandora and the Flying Dutchman, which also starred James Mason. Her boyfriend, Frank Sinatra, was in New York at the time. When he heard about the affair he jumped on a plane to Barcelona and got a taxi to S'Agaro – 80 kilometres up the coast from Barcelona. The locals still talk about the punch up in the foyer of La Gavina Hotel that followed his arrival there. Sinatra hightailed it back to New York the same day, sans Ava Gardner, which confirms that when a crooner confronts a bullfighter there is really no contest.

9    Catalans are heavily into shit.  It permeates many aspects of life – art, politics, folk-lore, literature – to a degree unusual in any other society I can think of.  The caganer, a squatting, bare-buttocked figurine in a floppy Catalan cap, is an indispensable part of all nativity scenes. Joan Miró, that most lauded of Catalan painters whose motif for La Caixa is prominent in the High Street or central plaça of every Catalan town, clearly had a thing about the stuff. "Eat well, shit forcefully, and you won't have to worry about dying\*, is how the well-known saying has it.

10   There's a Catalan town called Llívia that is completely surrounded by France, a bit like the old West Berlin without the wall, and in another country of course. All right, it's not actually much like the old West Berlin.  It's a very nice town with lots of Romanic architecture, high up in a Pyrenean valley, which got overlooked in a treaty between France and Spain at the end of the Thirty Years' War.  Under the terms of the treaty, the upper part of the valley and all the villages in it were ceded to France, but Llívia was considered to be a town, not a village, so it stayed Catalan, i.e. Spanish.  The devil is in the detail, you see.  To this day you have to drive along a two-kilometre corridor through France to get to it.  The Thirty Years War was an episode in European history I always had trouble getting my head around during A levels, probably because it wasn't taught by Mr Pitt, who only bothered himself with British history, but an uninspiring young upstart of a teacher whose name I don't remember.  I'm sure he never told us about Llívia in any of his lessons.

\*Menjar be i cagar fort / i no tingues por de la mort

It's a curious historical fact, incidentally, that FC Barcelona, which consciously brands itself as the heart-beat of Catalan nationalism, was founded by a Swiss businessman. His real name was Hans Gamper, but his Christian name is always given as the definitively Catalan Joan, pronounced Djooan. The first president of the club was an Englishman, and the first match they played was against a bunch of English expatriates, which they lost one nil, though Barça spin masters are quick to point out some Barça members played for the expatriates' team, presumably to make up numbers. With that kind of pedigree, I don't know why they haven't applied to play in the Premier League. That really would be one in the eye for Madrid. Presumably if it happened we'd see els culers* waving banners saying: CATALUNYA IS NOT SPAIN.

> *(A nickname which originates from the Barça fans' habit of sitting on the wall of their first stadium on Carrer Indústria in Eixample district. From the outside a passer would see a long row of overhanging backsides - 'culés' being the word for arses.)

*    *    *    *

## WHEN PHILLIPA BROWN MET AVA GARDNER

They arrived about mid-day to find Ava, who was much smaller than either of them had expected, gazing out to sea. There was a streak of dried bird-shit on her shoulder. Phillipa forgot her headache for a moment and said she looked sorry for herself and had maybe had a premonition in Tossa of how her life would turn out, but Richard said he thought not. He was a film buff, and impatient to add to his wife's education.

"It's a very under-rated movie, though the story is completely ridiculous. This Flying Dutchman fellow is doomed to sail the seven seas for eternity, or until he finds a woman who loves him enough to die for him. It's quite Wagnerian, not to say surreal, which makes more sense if you know the director, Albert Lewin, was a close friend of Man Ray and Max Ernst."

"Really?" said Phillipa. She had taken up a position by Ava's side and was trying to focus on something small inching its way over the horizon like a fragile, fluttering insect - a sail, surely. A white one. Or a tiny wing?

"Yes. As a matter of fact, it got a screening last year at the Tate Modern's Dali and Film season. Of course, there's also Jack Cardiff's marvellous cinematography to consider."

The slight queasiness Phillipa had been conscious of all morning gave way suddenly to the conviction she was about to be sick. "Fancy!" she heard herself say. The word was enough to trigger a vivid picture of her mother, in a characteristically distracted pose, holding an empty glass in one hand and a cigarette in the other. At the same time, she was overpowered by the unmistakeable and powerful smell of a familiar perfume. Phillipa reeled at the unexpectedness of it. Tiny points of light glinted and danced across the flat expanse of water in front of her.

Richard didn't see his wife's distress, because all his attention was on prising the top off his large, new, leather camera case. "There wasn't much surreal about our Ava," he went on, "but she was an amazing woman all right. The seventh child of a North Carolina share-cropper, twice married and twice divorced - to Mickey Rooney and Artie Shaw - before she and Sinatra got together."

The top of the case flew open and Richard reached inside for the camera. He peered short-sightedly at the lens settings, but didn't stop talking.

"He'd stayed put in Los Angeles when Ava first came over with the rest of the cast, but he soon got wind from his pals in the press she was fooling around. He jumped on the first plane to Barcelona and then took a taxi all the way here to Tossa. She was on set with James Mason when he arrived but he just marched right up to her and said: Show me the grease-ball."

"Gracious." Phillipa decided she wasn't going to be sick after all. "What happened then?" She found herself wondering what a share-cropper was, exactly. She was quite sure Richard would be able to tell her if she asked him. Not that I'm going to, she promised herself.

"Apparently she kissed him and told him not to be silly. But it was no joke. He was crazy about her, see? They got married a year later, about the time MGM finally got round to releasing Pandora. The marriage didn't last, of course, but Sinatra always said afterwards that Ava Gardner was the one true love of his life."

A child licking a strawberry ice-cream went past, flanked by a cross-looking couple, heads bowed in the heat. Phillipa felt better now, but her head was still throbbing. She put her hand against Ava's slender neck and gently stroked the smooth, hot bronze. She pictured the hotel room as she and Richard had left it that morning, and the tiny plastic bride on the bedside table, still sticky with marzipan.

"Who was the grease-ball, then?" she asked quickly.

"Mario Cabre - a genuine, 24-carat bullfighter who played the part of one in the movie. I've been gored often, but Ava's pierced me more than the horn of any bull. Here! In the heart!" Richard thumped his chest. "That's what he told the Barcelona paparazzi, anyway."

Phillipa gulped. "Oh!"

"He was a terrible actor but a big ladies' man, apparently. A real charmer. He had a huge reputation around these parts back in the fifties."

"Did Ava talk about what went on between them?"

"At first she denied anything had. But later, in her autobiography, she described romantic nights in Tossa filled with stars, and alcohol, and waking up in Cabre's bed…" Richard paused, then laughed. "Now look here Phillipa, don't go getting ideas. I don't want you setting your sights on one of these local Johnies. You were being a sight too pally with that waiter last night for my liking!"

"Fat chance," said Philip wearily. "I can't speak the sodding language, remember?"

"That didn't stop Ava," said Richard cheerfully. "Stand next to her and hold still, will you. And for goodnesss sake, smile." He pointed the camera.

Phillipa looked over his shoulder, to the line far in the distance that divided the sky from the sea. She thought fleetingly of the redeeming power of love, and the nature of eternity. "No, I don't suppose it did," she said.

## 13. VIRAL ATTRACTION - PORTUGAL

Portugal. A caller came to the art school door. I wasn't expecting anyone – just arrived a few days ago, we didn't know a soul.

Weathered, black tousled hair, slim. Late thirties? Almost athletic. There was only me, just back from my first game of tennis with the ex-pats, not yet showered or changed. The rest had got the early bus to Seville for a day trip, long day trip. I'd opted for the tennis.

I had one workable phrase of Portuguese, so spoke clearly. 'No-one here (holding the door wide). Empty. Fala Inglès?'

'Of course. I work here sometimes. Model for the art people. The courses start in a few weeks, I came to see if there was any, you know - activity. Are you the first group? You're early.'

'No, we're not art people. Using it out of season that's all. You speak good English.'

One of the artists in our friendship gang had found the ad: art school in the Algarve for residential courses. Ten double rooms around courtyards (plural), a pool, lounges, kitchens and a studio. But no winter courses. She rang them. February - maybe into early March? Just the facility, no classes. We could fill it. It would be some additional income for you...

'Is it OK if I check the studio?'

In our sixties, some younger. Early retirees.

'Go ahead. I was making coffee. Will the classes be taking place, with the virus? We've been checking our flights out.'

'Portugal's OK.' She made her way through. I sat it out in the lounge with the cafetière and poured her one as she came back. She picked it up.

'The pigs who use this place – come and look.'

I hadn't been in. It looked OK to me, just needed some tables moving, they were easy enough, foldable. Maybe a sweep. Pots and brushes rinsing.

'All think they're Van Gogh. Make a mess, look crazy – great art will come.'

'I've seen you, I think. The portrait in the lounge. Is that you?'

'Yeh, last year. One of them did it and gave it to me, like a presentation. He was not happy when I wrote my phone number on it and pinned it up. Publicity. He didn't like his work to be the same as a commercial artist.'

'It's quite good.'

'Mmm. Maybe I take it back and use it somewhere in town. Are you sure they're cancelling - did they tell you?'

'They don't contact us about the classes. Like I said, we've got the place out of season. What will you do if they do?'

'Bad news for Anna. What about your group? You said you have artists. Book me – I'll come and clear the studio. Free. Free for the clear-up, you just pay the modelling fee.'

'Not me Anna – can't draw.'

'That's what art classes are for. I model – I pose for you. Other people will show you, all helping each other. Or I could draw you. Can you hold pose, do you know how?'

'I'd have to charge you. How much is it, by the way?'

'Forty-five. But I'm experienced – you couldn't charge that.'

'Isn't there a premium for fresh young debutants on their first assignment?'

'New model bonus, yeh? Smart. I have to check you over first though. Thanks for the coffee. Tell your friends to give me a ring.'

It was just me. The emptiness of the place rang in my ears. I shuffled around for a while, picking at pistachios, then went to shower. I had a bit of a plan, a lazy plan, to go to the town of Loulé – train to Faro, then bus. About an hour. We'd been to the big carnival there, when the streets were so crowded you could hardly move. But it looked interesting, worth revisiting on a quiet day. A street sign had caught my eye: "Pólo Museologico dos Frutos Secos". Seriously? I'd googled it when we got back. It didn't have its own page, but there was a reference to another museum: "Worth a visit if you are exploring Loulé, unlike the dried fruit museum down the road which is very lacking in content (though free)."

I had to go.

Faro was quiet, and although the bus station almost adjoined the rail station I felt like a stroll and a morning beer. The day was warming up. Actually it was no longer morning, nowhere near morning in fact, and I slipped into lunch mode. Which came with a half litre of tinto. I loafed around the pedestrian streets for a while and took the train back, frutos secos moved to the back burner. It would be nice to put something on the table for the travellers when they got back, just cold stuff with maybe some boiled pota- toes. I'm not good in the kitchen when people are around, Ellie neither. We started doing breakfast together when we were both retired, but over time we developed ends. Mine was the coffee and toast end. Sometimes I'd stay into her zone to cut an avocado, say, and she'd chase me away with light curses. After some further time she made an incursion into my end and occupied it. 'I can do this, go and look at your emails.' I thought, OK, good plan, I'll clear up after, which generally took longer so it was still a fair division, until we clashed over dishwasher technique and she took over that as well.

But I get it. And so pass a pleasant hour in my own quiet company setting the joined tables for twenty and chopping lettuce.

My phone goes.

'Ellie. Hey - how was Seville?'

'Dom, listen – all is not well. They've stopped us on the Spanish side and taken us to Hueva. We've got to be tested. On the way back can you believe, we've had the whole day to spread it assuming someone had it. They're isolating us for two days they say till they get the results. It's a kind of hostel. They won't let us out to get food. Looks like an asylum centre of some kind, god knows what we're supposed to sleep in. Dom? Are you there?'

I'm there – here – but struck dumb, gobsmacked. I'm actually thinking about how to clear the food.

'It's – that's dreadful... I suppose two days isn't so bad. Overall, I mean. They must surely let you out, to get toiletries and stuff. Can you share for tonight?'

'They won't let us. They've got security people with masks and visors, you can't believe it. Anyone would think... and I didn't bring my charger.'

We strung banal thoughts together for a few more minutes and ended the call. There was nothing to be done

105

other than let things take their course. I looked at the food. Well, might as well take a plateful and get myself comfortable. I finished the day reading in unimaginable almost audible silence, working my way down a bottle of Douro Valley red.

*       *       *       *

Lovely morning chorus of birdsong punctuated by the cracked croak of a cockerel somewhere nearby, senior by the sound of it, in need of a lozenge. Actually he's probably in good shape, relatively, it's the canaries in balcony cages the size of a toaster that need help, all trilling endlessly for a mate. And clear blue sky. There are messages and video clips from the Spanish exiles, trapped in their cages in Hueva. I can't be of use. I'll have a couple of eggs and some coffee – see if I can caffeine a bit of constructive input into the mix in the course of time.

I'm good with eggs. Five minutes then straight under the cold tap for a quick douche usually does it, into the eggcup, consume. Shuffling sound in the doorway, but I'm running the tap.

'Are they back yet?'

'Fucking hell, you gave me a… what are you doing here?'

One of our gang, carrying the hangover of all time by the look of it. Face fiery red, robe skew-wiff and very open at the top. She's a mess.

'Didn't feel good so I told him to go without me. Is it still Tuesday?'

'It's Wednesday morning. You must know what's going on – you've checked your phone, yeh?'

'Got some texts and missed calls, I need to get my contacts in first. There enough coffee?'

'Sure, sure… Oh. Shit. You've got it. Haven't you? The Covid thing. Get back to your room, now. You – sorry… Sorry – I mean you need to isolate yourself, quickly. You go up: open the window wide, clear the table by the bed, but not your phone – keep that on the table – and I'll literally cover my face and nip in with coffee. Please.'

Her eyes unfocussed – contacts not in, and virus. Perfect storm. God she looks ugly. I can't nudge her along. Her fevered mind is struggling to get on the register.

'They're still in Spain, the authorities kept them back for testing. All – the whole bus. You'll see when you get your eyes in. They'll be a couple of days. You need to go now, really. I'll bring the coffee in five.'

She turned without a word and took herself off. My eggs still in the sink, getting cold.

She took to her room for three days - two nights, three days. I brought her soup, tea, and savoury biscuits. I'd remove the things she'd used, put the new stuff down and exit. We had no conversations until I collected her plate at lunchtime on the third day. She asked for a sandwich and more tea.

'Hey - getting better… you look better, definitely.' I'm backing out all the same, the room's foetid. 'Maybe have a shower later? See if you fancy coming downstairs. Open your window when you come down, yeh? And put the fan on. Change the air. And turn the bed down…'

Rock'n'roll, the girl's been nursed back to health. I decide to upgrade from the cold meats and cheese I've been grazing on ever since the call that the gang weren't coming back. And still aren't - no word from the Spanish medical people. Ellie's calls from other people's phones until someone comes up with a compatible charger. They're all going stir crazy over there, the rooms are almost airless, there's no communal space or cooking. They're given supermarket bags with an assortment of dry snacks and carton drinks, and kept apart from each other except for a bit of supervised exercise outside in the evening when they can talk, but only on the move. Grim, but unhelpful to make it my problem. I decide to take a little trip to Pingo and cook something.

Pingo is our corner convenience supermarket. When you go in you're hit by the stink of salt cod, big opened-out spatchcocks of it lie in bins. I'm told if you soak it and rinse it, it looks and tastes exactly the same as fresh cod. Conveying my order takes perseverance, but I get the rigid high-smelling thing into a bag and back to our place.

She's not around yet. I google: "Soak the salted cod in cold water for 24 to 48 hours…" I stick it in a bowl and fetch us a takeaway from the Punjabi place. She leaves most of hers and heads back to bed, giving me a dilemma - I hate throwing usable food away, but should it sit in the fridge with the rest of the perishables? But there's a smaller one I remember in the back-up kitchen. I wipe it out and switch on, food back in the punnets, self-isolating.

I knew I'd got it the following morning when I went to make myself a tea. Our group is more or less evenly divided between basic tea and Earl Grey. If the inner packet is removed from the box it only takes a sniff to distinguish them, but I was unable to. I held respective bags under my nose and sniffed so hard I almost ingested them, but no good, so I took a guess and went for one of them, assuming I'd be more successful with taste. But no - it might as well have been hot water. Or the cod water from the bowl behind me, I realised I couldn't smell that either even though the thing had been soaking all night. During the plague, the Black Death, it's reported that people lost taste and smell. Or, in a variation, would sometimes say they smelled a sweetness in the air, which wasn't evident to other people.

What is it about the human race that every episode exposing our vulnerability has to be girdled with a concoction of good acts and heroism? As if people would choose to be heroic if there was an option of simply going home after a good day's work. The villagers of Eyam, their heroic self-isolation has become mythological, there are novels written about it, films, whereas in fact when villagers tried to leave they were driven back, pelted with stones.

I left her a note and took myself to back to bed. It wasn't too bad at that point, no worse than a hangover, which I probably had anyway having knocked off another bottle before retiring - just the tea thing that sent up alarm signals. It became three days for me as well, finally. Sweating like a tap, rabid, and numb with hypothermia at the same time. My treatment similar - iced drinks and dry biscuits - with the exception of a hot water bottle which did nothing medically but served as a kind of comforter. As the first signs of my recovery appeared, though not to me, she roused me from the bed like a grouse beater, kettled me into the shower, unearthed some clean garments from our drawers, wrapped me in a blanket and chased me out into the sunshine where I passed a period between wake and sleep being thawed or cooled to room temperature as she serviced the room. Strangely, I craved for beer.

Myself and the room dealt with in the same brutal but efficient manner, she came back up after several minutes with a couple of Sagres. They went down quick. She brought up two more. She'd put a robe on, a towelling thing, and swimsuit. She drew up a lounger, opening the robe to catch some sun.

It's difficult to categorise Lou, she's elusive, and so are her looks. She and her partner had both spent their working lives at the same PRU - the same pupil referral unit. These guys are all barking - they have a reputation for going rogue after a while, assuming they weren't from the outset. A bunch of disruptives and trouble-makers, impossible to train or retrain, but great with the kids. Her chap, Karl, had received verbal and written warnings from the authority, they were both vague about what rules he had failed to observe, or simply broken. Somehow he'd managed to get a deal to go early when deals were no longer being done. The implication was that he had dirt on the PRU and procedures therein, and his release was in the interests of both parties. Built like a cage fighter, liberally studded - ears, nose, nipples, that we know about. He now replicates the role of rogue and loose cannon within our group, having us thrown out of a balti house in the Lye, fortunately well off our doorstep, and barred from a town pub, a Marston's house which we'd strayed into on (drunken) impulse, so again, not a regular of ours. Confirming my sense that it's all quite carefully choreographed, largely for his own amusement.

Lou could be described as a silver Goth - sans silver - an aged Goth: her hair always jet black and short. Strong-featured, a Gothic Annie Lennox, or maybe Jamie Lee Curtis, her looks would divide a room. If she walked into a fashion store she could just as easily be a high-end client, a shoplifter or storewalker. No metallic facial accessories, in contrast to Karl, though she does have a very small, distinct scar running downwards via the fine downy hair on the left side of her upper lip. A disfiguration, that one might describe as gangsta, as sexy, if one were in a certain mood, for example two or three drinks in.

We leaned together to clip bottles and she rolled towards me slightly, exposing the full tattoo down her thigh. There had been glimpses, but she wasn't a person for self-display, her clothing preference usually layered and black. Knowing her it could have been something like Bollox to the Poll Tax, done in her twenties on a stoned trip some-where exotic, concealed ever since. But it was a dragon, a wonderful writhing thing in green and red, with multiple gills and tendrils, frills, fangs, fins and a ferocious arrowed tongue.

I felt what I think is known as the bat-squeak of desire, these were thighs that would squeeze and not let go.

'Welsh..? I didn't know.'

'No, boyo. Idealism of youth. To the Chinese it symbol-ises wisdom, good luck, and strength of will. I was into that stuff.'

She eased the gown off and settled herself. I dragged another lounger over. A few notes from a tune came into my head, something familiar and obscure, when I tried to concentrate and push it along it morphed into an inane chart-topper from way back. I pulled my cap over my eyes and let the sun dandle me.

Pentangle. Yes, it was Pentangle. How long has it been? God they were good. The song still eluded me, and the album, though we'd had it in vinyl. Buff cover, five-pointed star, I could see it. As I stood up to find my laptop the world before my eyes darkened and I had to sit down sharply, making the underside of the lounger swell like a plum pudding. I gathered myself and fetched it, along with a couple more beers.

It was Willy O' Winsbury.

'And she's cast off her berry-brown gown
She stood naked upon the stone
Her apron was low and her haunches were round,
Her face was pale and wan.'

Those were the lines that had got stuck in my brain, an observation not shared with my co-lounger who had cast off her own gown. I played the full album, driving her away a few bars through the first track, and since the mood had taken me, passed some further time playing Neil Young and Crazy Horse.

The sun was low now. I drained the bottle, slid a bit further down the lounger and closed my eyes. I woke to semi-darkness, feeling dire. She'd cooked the cod and was nudging me to come down for some. The thought made me want to heave, I headed for the room muttering inaudible apologies. Our time with each other was being punctuated by a series of lovingly prepared but uneaten meals.

But in the morning I was the first one up, ravenous and raring to go. I fried up half a complete chorizo, eggs, tomatoes and soaked up the fat with fried bread. A pot full of coffee, and squeezed orange juice. She came in on cue, must have smelled the food and heard the clatter. I was manic.

Looking fresh and summery, light blue t-shirt and shorts, dragon disappearing into.

'They're back today!' She smothered the eggs with salt. 'Have you checked your phone? Don't worry, Ellie rang me a few times since you've been laid up, I've been giving out your medical news, but no update this morning, you can do that. Release time ten o'clock for them, so back here early afternoon. Let's do them a bloody banquet, they've had a shocker. What drink is there - have we got champagne?'

Shit, I hadn't even checked my phone - must have got out of the habit. It rang as I aimed my first mouthful, I rammed it in anyway. She was hyper with happenstance. 'Can I ring you back?' Doesn't go down too well, but when you're gagging to eat... Lou's gesture to put it in the warming drawer given a firm brush-off.

We have a long phone call, finally; things looking good, they've all got themselves showered, packed what little they had with them onto the coach and are ready to head for home, home base. The call ends with their departure - it doesn't need to, but evidently they've bonded after some initial misunderstandings with the hostel staff, or guards, who in the final analysis had only been doing their jobs, and tearful farewells are in order.

I smarten up for my first outing in what seems a long time. We make one hell of a smart couple, heading purposefully to Pingo, I almost forget myself and take her hand. We wheel a trolley back - the art school trolley, they use it to load the kit when they go out painting in the open.

But good news turns to bad at a stroke. Ellie in tears, they've been stopped at the border again, this time the Portuguese side. It's taken a full week for the tests to come through negative; the Spanish border lot have waved them straight through, can't wait to be rid of them, but the Portuguese come on the coach to do routine temperature checks and have decided Fiona is feverish. They're being required to spend a further fourteen days in quarantine before entry is granted.

There's a tense stand-off between the Spanish and Portuguese, and no-one's allowed off even for toilets until decisions on their new destination have been made and formalities done. Negotiations are underway, I'm in present time here - it appears Karl has appointed himself leader and is trying to strike a deal from the coach door. He seems to have been successful. After intermittent pauses she tells me they've agreed to a vacant hotel, the Spanish border people, instead of returning them to the hovel they've passed the last week in. Re-testing and processing will be a formality the Spanish assure them, the Portuguese are coños, and they'll be rapidly back for resumption of holiday. Applause in the background. Give people a dollop of really shit news and anything less will send them into euphoria.

So, hellfire, once again we have food for many on the go, there are two whole chickens in the oven for a start. Things need to be digested slowly and thoroughly at this point, and I don't just mean the food.

It's too late to take them out, they can cook on low for while. We need to get out, to go somewhere, anywhere. We've both had it so we feel safe to. But it's daunting to discover how completely closed the place is. The ferry's still running, we head for the islands, but the only travellers are locals with bags of shopping and grim faces. Who'd have thought we'd long for fellow-tourists? We're severely out of place; we get the next one back.

The smell of chicken is delicious, we decide to do it with boiled spuds and salad and eat on one of the terraces with a fresh bottle of wine. The act of selection is interrupted by a fierce knock on the door. It can't be them, surely? And it's too urgent for Anna. Who else do we know?

Four men - one in uniform, one part-uniformed, the other two behind in manual clothes.

'Department of National Security señor, we have to requisition this place.'

He steps in - it's theirs already.

'You can't, it's occupied. There are twenty of us.'

'Yes. Art school. Needed for isolation unit, we have the document.'

He holds it up, knowing we can't scrutinise anyway.

'Tomorrow, por favor? We were just about to eat.'

I'm thinking, town hall first thing, get the misunderstanding sorted out.

'Now señor. Tomorrow the first patients come.'

'There are twenty of us. Where will we go - the hotels are shut. And there's a complication…'

'Friends in Hueva for test, understand. We have places - apartments - but not together. You are the lucky ones, yours in the town centre, others not - not all. You must pack your possessions and we will take you.'

Lou steps in.

'You can't do this, we don't accept. If you just wait a couple of weeks - before if flights can be changed - we'll all be gone. Back to UK. Then it's all yours.'

'No Señora. Pack now please. No couple of weeks. We will pack the other and store somewhere, government place maybe, or take to apartments for them so they have on arriving. Please…'

He steps back and indicates. We have no choice.

I stagger down with Ellie's and my stuff, all crammed in as I've scooped it up. Lou takes longer, two of them rush forward to help her. Great minds - we've both thought to bring those limp rucksacks, the kind you take with you just for the day, for the food and drink, and stuff them full. We'll come back for the rest, we Inform the boss man, but he shakes his head. In whispers, for no evident reason, we make heartbreaking choices. With what's left behind they'll eat as well as us, we might as well just set the table and eat together.

Maybe not. They take our luggage firmly from us and heave it with all the rest into a well-dented vehicle with faded municipal livery. They've gutted the place in an hour, except for the kitchen where a substantial amount of succulent hot food awaits our departure obviously. Not even invited to check the other rooms for possible over-looked items. We hunch in with the cargo of cases and are driven the narrow cobbled roads to a shabby unit of flats. Wordless interest from the balconies. We hump and scrape our stuff up the stairs, led by the driver scrutinising a handful of keys, assistance not in his job description. He finds ours and gets it open. It's basic, but has been cleaned at least. He hovers - not for a tip surely. Just making sure we establish ourselves and don't do an imme-diate runner I guess. He clearly can't show us round, he hasn't seen it himself. Waits while we try taps and open doors - the two internal doors. It's a one bedroom place.

We turn to him.

'No good Señor, no bom.' I point to each of us and cross my hands. 'Not together... Not married.'

His face is blank, like a cast. I motion kissing, then cross my hands again. He shrugs and turns to go. Lou takes her eyes off him to weigh up the choices and he gives me a little conspiratorial thumbs up and leaves. He figured that one out the bugger, language or no language.

We stand there in mild shock and take it in. There isn't even a sofa to kip on. A couple of armchairs with cushions that could be laid on end for a short person, no extra bedding, at a cursory glance. There's a wardrobe though, that's a possibility.

'Tell you what,' I say jovially, 'do you snore?'

'Don't even think about it.'

'Too late. Four short cushions in a floor mosaic won't do it for me. Are you going to offer?'

Her scowl doesn't shift.

'I binged on a TV series once, boredom choice, then got hooked. Watched the whole lot on catch up, pseudo-therapy for couples, they were supposed to patch up their marriages by being paired with each others' partners for a few weeks. A way of exploring their behaviours in the close company of a different person. So the programmers put them in amazing condos and send them on activities together to see how they'll bond…'

Her hands are on her hips now, in that pose that says you're wasting your time.

'But there's a catch. Single bedroom. They have to negotiate their sleeping arrangements together, that's the first situation they give them. And obviously the money shot for viewers, they have night cameras to check the goings-on. But the thing is, nothing really goes on, even if there's an attraction. Most of the blokes give the woman the bed and kip on the settee. Some share the bed head to toe, some head to head; a couple of times they build a row of cushions between them. What d'you reckon?'

'I reckon you fancy your luck.'

'And I reckon I'm not kipping on those, and I'm not a rapist, so unless you fancy your luck I don't see a problem.'

She lets it drop and starts to get some things out of her cases. Wrestles with a hollow drawer that won't open straight and puts the first things in. I leave our bags and decide to get the food in the fridge. It's rank. There are no cleaning agents except for a several months old washing up liquid bottle with a scrape in the bottom, less liquified that it probably was originally, the top clogged, it'll need a fork prong. No cloth, no kitchen roll nor toilet paper. I find a t-shirt from our wash bag and use that, just to get the stuff in and switch it on. We do a quick tally of what's needed and I dive out to Pingo, detour past the art school obviously, some lights are on now. There are piles of folded bedding waiting for allocation I guess, numerous empty and half-drunk wine and beer bottles, ours, and glasses on the tables.

Our new place looking a bit more cared for when I return, she's got her cases under the bed and essential stuff in drawers. Steamed up like the Kew Gardens palm house, she's managed a shower and changed into something loose. Loose and sexy. The window open - steam gets sucked out as I close the door. The table set, it had flaps that open out, not too evenly, she's put the chicken and wine on the central part, the more stable part. Salad and spuds in the kitchen, kitchenette, along with plates and cutlery which might also slide off.

She tells me to watch my elbows in the shower, it's very confined, like the shower in a caravan.

My phone goes. Ellie. There's panic in Spain, Fiona's confirmed with the virus and has been hauled off to a hospital. The rest informed that strict isolation is extended by another fourteen days and will be extended further in the event of new cases.

The hotel they've been allocated is adequate but not staffed, the same food bags are delivered as before and left in the entry. It's an open prison in comparison, they have access to the kitchen - i.e., haven't been denied access. It's been cleared of food but they've found a catering tin of instant coffee. The smell, having a remote association with real coffee, gives them a remote association with comfort. They have to drink it black, but there is sugar, and their sandwiches when they come can be toasted. But there is massive agitation over medication and other essentials which were still there in their rooms in the art school as the trip was only scheduled for a day. People have run out of tablets and whatever, they can't get anyone to supply them. A torrent of examples follows, her voice rising up the panic scale. On top of this there are UK issues: various pets, small businesses mainly from home, older and younger dependants - none of these can be left indefinitely, what's going to happen?

I take a long breath and tell her to email me a precise list and I'll see what I can do. Haven't got the faintest clue what I can do, what can anyone? But words like this have a calming effect I find. Did when the kids were young anyway. 'Don't forget the address of the hotel…' Like I'm going to pop everything neatly in a box and send it same-day delivery.

We look at each other. 'It's a fucking mess. Shall we eat?'

The meal is not as ambient as I'd hoped. The plates slide towards us, we decamp to the armchairs and eat from our laps. The Spain situation doesn't help digestion. We have to think of something - there are our friends' belongings in unattended apartments all over the town. Apart from retrieving various immediate needs there's the question of vulnerability. We need to get them moved somewhere safe, but who do we know? The municipal jobsworths were royally unhelpful, and if they're still at the art school are probably pissed by now. We had to leave a lot of drink.

I remember Anna.

'There was a life model, she called when you were sleeping off your infection - sleeping anyway, I didn't even realise you were there at the time. Wanted to know when the art classes were starting. Her picture was on the board, remember? There was a phone number scribbled on it.'

'So how do we get it? There won't be anyone at the school now will there?'

'It's not there now, she took it. But no problem, she left a card with me…'

It was in my wallet. I put the plate on the floor and found it.

'Anna…'

'Si, que esta?'

'From the art school. Dominic. Remember? You came round.'

'Yeh, sure. You got an art class for me?'

'No Anna, that's not going to happen is it? And if it could happen, it can't. They've kicked us out of the art school. Council security guys, they want it for virus victims.' It occurred to me as I was speaking they want it for quarantine, which is what's happening to our lot a few hours down the road in Spain. With a bit more luck we could have all been quarantined in the place we'd booked, which is kind of why we booked it anyway.

'So where are you now? You want me to help you find a place, yeh?'

'No, we've got somewhere - they've put us in an apartment in town.'

'All? Twenty? What apartment?'

'No. Er, no, just two of us. The rest have been held in Spain. One of them caught the virus so they're in isolation there. No return for two weeks minimum.'

'The Spanish are coños. Where's the apartment?'

'In town. Not far from Pingo - the other side from the art school.'

'Ha. Near me too. So what have you rang me for? Bored? You want to draw me? Sure. Here - my place - no problem. But not two of you together. You, or the other guy. One at a time.'

'Very good Anna - setting boundaries for safe sex, wise move…'

'NO!! Corona virus. Filthy bastard. I'm hanging up on you…'

'Wait. Wait Anna - only joking, it just came out. Silly.' Silly? Fucking perverse, I need counselling. 'Please. We have to find their bags. The guys who took them said they were going to some council storage place or the apartments. They've got apartments ready for our group when they get back, eventually, I think that's where the cases have gone. The other guy's a she by the way. Can you help?'

'You kidding? They won't give addresses to me. Personal data, all that stuff. You have to speak to them yourself, take I.D., maybe they help, maybe not. They have hands full with other business right now.'

'We can't speak Portuguese can we? We'll get some little time-server behind the desk who's got three words of English knowing our luck. Could you come with us.'

'No! Not allowed, don't you get it? Take a phrase book, try and speak Portuguese if you think we're so dumb. Any of your group speak Portuguese? How many?'

'That's different Anna…'

'Why? Small country - that your reason? How many Spanish speaking then?'

'I think we've got a couple. But…'

'Yeh - can order a drink and a steak. You expect us - taxi drivers, police, on the trains, shop people. Not educated like you but they just open their mouths and out it comes, yeh? God's language. Given by God. Anyway, forget that - there are people dying, from this town, who lived here their whole lives. You're not top priority. Shocking for you I know…'

Shit, I've done a Larry David here - got myself in deep water when I really didn't need to.

'Anna, I'm sorry - I've offended you. It came out wrong, don't take any notice.'

'Always coming out wrong with you, eh? Email the addresses, I'll try. It's gonna cost you.'

'We don't have addresses. They just scooped every-thing up and drove us here. No-one said a thing - we wouldn't have heard them if they did, with the engine, it was one hell of a bone-shaker.'

'I'll call you in the morning. Two hundred euros. I speak to someone - try and get the keys for a couple of hours. Hundred for him, hundred for me. If I don't get them, fifty for me anyway, for trying. Agree or not?'

'OK. Agree.'

Having taken the first step softens the tension. We scoop plates out of the way and set about the booze. We rescued a good selection, modest on quantity but high on quality. Gin, on top of the beer and wine, port, campari, and a decent whisky one of the guys who'd come over by car brought with him. The tonics are Pingo best, a bit sharp on the palate but Lou concocts herself a gin & campari with a slosh of it. Mine's the whisky, stiff, a Glenfarclas fifteen year which no-one had managed a sniff of up to now in spite of it being shelved in communal territory. There are certain drinks that require an invitation. What occasion he'd been waiting for I've no idea. I look across.

'This is cosy…'

'Be careful what you wish for Señor…'

I look aghast. Theatrically.

'You're like an open book. You realise he'd cripple you if he found out. He broke a guy's nose once and that was just for hitting on me, we didn't get round to actual contact.'

'He wouldn't have to find out. Necessarily. Not that anything… If it was kept under wraps.'

(The king has been a prisoner,
And a prisoner long in Spain,
And Willy of the Winsbury
Has lain long with his daughter at home…)

'Sure. These things have a habit of getting out though, don't they..'

'You sound like an experienced campaigner. You have the occasional affair?'

'Not really. Did a swap with another couple when we were younger. Just a holiday thing I thought, but he had to have her - like, possess her, the idiot. Went off with her for three months.'

'Quite a holiday then, for him. But you took him back…'

'He was persuasive, fucking charmer. Plus I was pregnant, that sort of tipped the scale I guess.'

'Shit. But you were sure it was Karl's? I mean - sorry - Jake. He's definitely…'

'Yeh, he's Karl's, can't you tell? Besides, my guy was black. She was white though, Essex girl, the cow. Never heard from them again, obviously, I don't know if they stayed together.'

I reached down and poured another dram or two. That was quite a revelation. Our gang tended to stick to safer ground.

'How about you? Had any affairs?'

'Couple. On residentials, so both self-contained.'

'And Ellie?'

'Doubtful. No smoking guns. Can't ever know though can you…'

She downed the lot and sucked on the lemon.

'Do you realise how hateful you sound? How furtive? If I was married to you they'd find you in a shallow grave.'

'What - just on the assumption? You wouldn't know…'

'Yes. On the assumption. Smug bastard.'

She gets up and makes herself a fresh drink. Big fresh drink, bright red and more-ish, I ask for a sip. As she holds it out to me I put my hand lightly on her thigh.

There's a hiatus. She doesn't move away.

'We might regret this…'

(Oh was it with a lord or a duke or a knight,
Or a man of wealth and fame,
Or was it with one of my serving men
That's lately come out of Spain?)

I follow the dragon to its downy lair. The unforgettable sound of breath catching. She eases herself onto my lap. First full kiss, that wonderful closeness of a completely new lover, the consummation of breaths. Breath is the sexiest thing, the first hint of inside, of her interior.

The chair has a hard skeleton, we take ourselves to the bed, no wall of cushions built or contemplated, and burrow into each other.

\*　　　\*　　　\*　　　\*

(The king has called his merry men all,
By thirty and by three,
Says, Fetch me this Willy of Winsbury,
For hang-ed he shall be.)

\*　　　\*　　　\*　　　\*

I wake up horny as hell. I love it so much better in the morning, unfolding together, mingling warmth. But a ping emanates from her phone. I know the situation in Spain requires prompt attention, but this strikes me as extreme.

'They've sent the list to me. Don't want the likes of you passing on their private circumstances. Nor any of the other men, before you get irate. This is strictly a lady thing.'

'What about the blokes' privacy? Not a consideration? What if someone's on viagra or something?' It's not male pride that's at issue really, it's that she's flipped straight over into management mode.

'I'm going to put some coffee on and go through it. There's a lot here, we'll need boxes.'

As she busies herself I take a look. After a token display of exasperation she lets me go through it with her. I had no idea so many of us were on medication. Statins, steroids, urinary stuff, inhalers. Carol part-way through a course of antibiotics. Then secondary things like hearing aid batteries, contacts and saline solution. Requests for clothing and underwear across the board, makeup items, concern over essential ID documents and valuables, among them an almost full bottle of malt, and a guitar. Books and audio books also in big demand.

Specific worries over hire cars possibly incurring parking tickets or excess charges.

'What about you,' I say, 'you on any medication?'

She shakes her head. 'Not that I'd tell you. You?'

Negative. 'What d'you reckon - see if Anna can score us some weed?'

The email concludes with general angst about canines that'll pine away for dear mummy and daddy dog-persons, cat concerns less evident. There are bee hives going unattended, and the life and death matter of an exhibition-standard tropical aquarium. Gardens in general running to seed as nature but not their owners intended, some business issues, and deep human matters of pregnant daughters, senile relatives, grandchildren growing apart.

These we can't tackle. So the plan is - a brisk but decent breakfast, I phone Anna to see if she got anywhere with the addresses and keys. If yes, I go to Pingo for boxes; if no, we prepare ourselves to storm the town hall.

But she rings before we've got the rolls buttered. She has keys and addresses. There's no way we'll find them all, at least two are on the outskirts of Faro, and the keys have to be handed back on the guy's lunch break when he'll be off-site. So it has to be done now. One of us - the woman, not me, Anna says - with her in the car, windows down, she'll bring masks. Perfect. My jobs to put a bit of lunch out for later, get boxes parcel tape and marker pen, take aforementioned when full to post office and dispatch. Then hopefully we can take our leisure for a few days and go where impulse blows us…

I'm grounded enough to think about the down times though, and tell her to root me out a book, not too heavy and not pulp fiction. Like what, she says. I try to think what people were reading. Someone had the latest Anne Tyler, Siobhan I think, that'll do. Fairly gentle and domestic, no bullets, love conquers all. The literature of understated goodness. There was that one where they gather the whole extended family for an autumn leaves clear-up party, which one was it? Takes an entire chapter, but beautiful in itself. She's not Kingsolver, but you'd never throw a book of hers across the room in frustration. Find that one if you can I tell her.

We manage to get the whole lot into three half-dozen wine boxes, medication and bits wrapped up in clothing. I number them one, two and three over three in the hope they'll be charged as one lot, and head for the post place. There's seating, and three people in. Four attended windows, so I go directly to the free one.

'No Señor. Ticket...'

She points to a dispenser by the door, the tickets are like the ones you get at a supermarket deli counter. I drop the boxes to the side and get one. As I come back she points to a screen, I have to wait for my turn. When the number comes up I go back to the window.

'No Señor, this is window A, your ticket is for window C.'

They are all staffed but C is the only one taking customers. I sit and wait. Transactions are prolonged.

Finally I get to window C and explain my requirement. My simple requirement.

'You want to send Normal, or Express Señor?'

I tell him it must go Express.

'Moito bom, Express is cheaper.' He checks the address and writes it by hand on his forms; checks the second box and writes the address on new forms. I explain my hope that they will be classed as one delivery. He tells me quite impossible, they must be weighed and sent as separate items.

'Sender's address Señor?'

I don't know it.

'Sender's address is obligatory.'

There are now four new customers waiting it appears for window C. They seem untroubled as I phone Lou and wait for her to go down and outside to figure out our address.

'Same for all?'

He enters it on the three lots of forms. I'm exhibiting heroic restraint here.

'Email and phone please...'

'And email and phone for persons receiving.'

I give him Ellie's. He picks up the first box and weighs it. Weight copied down.

'Contents please.'

I have to check the number. It's the third box.

'Clothing.'

His expression changes.

'Export?'

'No, no. Personal clothing.' I identify the second box and tell him this too is personal clothing. He pushes it aside and carries on writing. Then we do the second box. The third - i.e. the first - I've decided to tell him is also clothing, to get the job done, but it weighs substantially heavier. Some personal medications I say. With clothing.

'Which medications Señor? Please give exact names.'

I get back to Lou and she goes through them. I give him each one; he calls the younger teller from window B over and she translates for him, for the forms.

'The first two boxes can go Express Señor. This must go through customs department for examination.'

Perversely, I'm pleased. It will get me away from the damned window.

'Can you direct me to the customs people por favor?'

'It must be done by the postal department.'

'And how long will it take, do you think?'

'Maybe a week, maybe less maybe more.'

'They are needed urgently.'

'We will request priority.'

'And if I send the other boxes separately as you suggest - how long, in your judgement?'

'They will all go together Señor, when the customs department is satisfied. As one lot. With customs clearance so no further delay.'

I scoop the boxes up. His expression registers no reaction to the voiding of the last twenty-five minutes of his time. There are now six people in the seating area, whose expressions don't register the change in circumstance either. No-one gets up, the screen is still showing my number.

Outside, it's become stinking hot. I need a think, mission complete failure won't look good. There's a green in front of a large chain hotel, not really a green, an area with a couple of trees and a bench in the shade they give. I dump the boxes and sit. Ring Anna, my first and only thought. She tells me she'll get back to me. I'm descended on by a street vendor, illegal in view of the lockdown, he has a cool box with cans of supermarket beer, takes three euros off me good luck to him. Beer on the warm side. I make the best of it and close my eyes for a while.

Anna's back on. 'Tonight the only possibility. Inland, not route national. My cousin knows someone who can fix it. Get you across. But must be tonight - different people will be on duty next week, we don't know them.'

'Across…'

'The river. River Guadiana, that's the border.'

'So - we cross the border, get the boxes to them, turn round and come straight back, yeh?'

'One only. Lou. Yes. How many boxes?'

'Three. Small. And - will there be a fee involved?'

'Sure. Eight hundred. COD. Is that how you say it?'

'Eight's high Anna. Very high. I can offer five. For a nearly a grand they could order the things themselves and have them delivered by Limousene.'

'Try then. Eight is a good deal. I got to pay a Portuguese guy, a Spanish guy, my cousin for setting up. And the borrow of Spanish security jackets.'

'Sorry?'

'How else you going to hand them over - throw over the fence?'

'OK, sure. And your fee? Included?'

'You don't pay me, they pay me, the guys who get you across.'

'But we pay them…'

'What you like, it's eight hundred. OK - seven-fifty. You want me to fix it or not?'

I tell her I need to consult, give me an hour, and put the issue to Ellie. She tells me they'll confirm after a pow-wow and get back as soon as they can.

I sit for a bit longer. The beer's warm on my tongue, I select a small palm-looking thing and water it. She rings on the way back, I prop myself against a wall to take it. Their verdict throws me: three-way split. Some for paying up, some for support in principle but not willing to pay more than four hundred, some against on principle, the principle of contravening regulations, specially when set by the host country. The compromise is that I should try the UK Consulate, there's an office in the Algarve, someone knows someone who knew someone who had to get them to help with a dispute. I say go ahead, why do you need us. They already have: the Spanish office is unhelpful bordering on rude, the Portuguese won't take a case from another country.

I get back in a state of pissed off-ness and slump down in the bony armchair to recount my afternoon. Lou's good, she gets a very cold beer and pours it into a glass so I can drink more at a time, much more, and as I'm doing so googles the consulate.

I ring, and get two Portuguese case workers with precise English, one after the other. The second more junior evidently, she's been handed the hot potato when the first one realises it can't be dismissed in a couple of minutes. But the kid's no fool, she puts me on hold for a bit, and the next person to speak to me is a jolly good old boy who sounds as if he could have served in the Raj. They must keep him in a cupboard in the event of more unusual cases that require a stiff dash of Britishness. He's wonderful on the medications, appears to have intimate knowledge of them all and utters appropriate words of sympathy as he jots them down. Then takes a long sigh.

'Obvious way forward would be to see if we can rouse some Spanish pharmacy chappies from their siesta and simply get them to do a delivery. All of these are basic drugs... Problem is, they've got themselves in a bit of a buggers' muddle over there. Going down like flies, Not sure they'll want to drop things for a few statins if you follow. Let me think.. Mmm. We can try the chaps at Faro and see if they might fast track your parcels for you. Can you get to Faro, do you think? Actually, looking at the time we may have to settle for tomorrow now. But a day here or there doesn't seem to make a lot of difference with these things, whatever the docs say. I often forget myself - just take two the next day, never a problem… Ah. No - tomorrow's a damned saint's day, pardon me, we'd be talking Friday. If they play ball.'

I thank him so much and say we would like to contact first thing Friday morning if we still need to avail ourselves of his services. He wishes us a very good evening and will look forward to our call.

Right. This is no good, I'm going to offer them a straight take it or leave it on the border crossing and knock the whole thing on the head. I don't do other people's problems.

They take it. I say to Lou I should go too, as I'm the bellwether here, but don't tell Anna when we make final arrangements. Lou offers their hire car when she arrives, which to our relief she accepts, the thought of her trying to make calls whilst driving her dusty old banger does not appeal. And accepts me riding shotgun. I think there was some kind of trust thing initially. I might have told her push comes to shove neither of us is that trustworthy…

We take the motorway to the border, then turn inland to Alcoutim where we're met by a rugged old boy who has a craft that will take a single car. Looking at the improvised arrangement to get us from the ramp to the deck we both wonder if we should have stuck with Anna's car, but make it across slightly downriver to a track which our riverain friend sets us down on at the third attempt.

It's dark now, a relief when we make it onto a proper road. The hotel they're at is in Trigueros just out of Hueva by the motorway, in our direction. The drive on the Spanish side has seemed much shorter.

We drive past a couple of times for a recky, stop round the corner to put the jackets on, there are only two but I'm not coming this far to stay in the car, Lou finds a high-vis thing in the boot, it'll be OK if I stay at the back, especially with half our faces covered by masks. She pulls over on the other side of the road, so the darkness hides its identity as a hire car. Two bored doorkeepers at the entrance, they cast their eyes languidly over the boxes. Three personnel, three small boxes, why give one man a job that three can do equally well. It's a concept they have familiarity with, they wave us in. Our reception follows the lines of the dispute: half a dozen rush to us, greet us enthusiastically and grab the boxes, some hang back and stare from a distance behind their masks, the rest remain in rooms. A hugely diverse group, you don't realise until the chips are down.

They have no drink to offer us, we should have thought, we had a fridge full, but bottled water is plentiful. Lou and I pair up with partners again while boxes are ripped open and plundered. Anna leans against a pillar and counts notes of several denominations that have been thrust at her.

I'm in the loo as Karl comes in.

'Get the bib off then..'

'Sorry?'

'Jacket. You don't think you're going back with her do you?'

'I think we have to, don't we?'

'Do we fuck. Get the jacket off.'

I simply hadn't considered it, how daft is that. I hand it over, it's his anyway. He puts it on and pulls the door open. Turns round as he goes through.

'You'd better not have…'

I chew on this, and realise the breathless feeling high in my chest is fear. When I come out the two of them have already set off. There is some agitation when the swap is perceived by the less participatory in the group, and we, myself and Ellie, opt for diplomacy and self-isolate in the room. It's fine, I'm knackered anyway, we just settle for spooning after a catch-up on various diverse and quirky behaviours not displayed among our gang in any previous circumstances. Ground rules for the longer term can be laid down in the morning.

*     *     *     *

I'm woken from deep sleep by my phone. It's Lou, they've been detained at Alcoutim and transferred to a police vehicle. They're now in custody in Faro. There's shuffling as she tells me.

'… fucking shit show. Who's fucking idea…'

'Karl, that's not helping… Give it to me.'

After some white noise Anna comes on.

'The boatman wasn't there, bastard. My cousin will kill him. He came one hour late. So do we wait quietly with headlights off? No. This Karl idiot wants dance music and a smoke, has the volume up, windows down. I guess someone figured it out, they were waiting when we got across. You guys got me in a big mess, you know that?'

'Well Anna - maybe; maybe your cousin should have been… Look, it's happened now. What will they do, do you know?'

'I heard them in the car saying five thousand euros, I

135

don't know if each of us or one fine all. I guess they're gonna interview us first.'

'OK. Let me see what I can do…'

'You? What the fuck? You gonna talk to the president?'

'Just give me a day or two. Get some sleep now, OK. Tell the others I'll be in touch.'

'You got some fuckin neck.'

Nice one Anna, nice to see you're keeping up with the action films. I wait till first thing Friday morning and ring my chum from the consulate. The interim taken up with lurid accounts of the group's engagement with Spanish offi-cialdom and subsequent straightened situation in holding pen and hotel, punctuated by my Kafka-esque cameo at Correios de Portugal, window C.

'"Redhead by the Side of the Road". Did you forget it? Sugar. I was on the last chapter. Anne Tyler…'

Friday. British Consulate.

'Good morning. English chaps under quarantine, supply lines cut off. Hadn't forgotten. Now - the question is, are our friends in Faro minded to help or hinder, hmm? Let's give them a try…'

'No. Sorry - ah, new development I'm afraid. We decided to skirt round the bureaucracy and nip across with the things by car. We had a bit of help from a local girl…'

'Good for you. Night-time raiding party, native intelli-gence, catch the buggers on the hop. Man after my own heart. When I was younger - let me see, when was it…'

'Yes. The thing is, I don't know if it registers, but I'm talking to you from Spain. I'm in the quarantine place with the others…'

'Aha. Couldn't avoid capture, eh? Don't tell em anything, my advice. Ha. Don't mind me. Sounds like you're up the proverbial creek. Hoping I can help I suppose.'

I ask if he can possibly convey to the authorities that it was a mercy mission. A plea for leniency. For clemency. My wording chimes with his. He tells me to stand by my post.

Back on before lunch.

'Fines scaled down to reflect exceptional circumstances. Lucky I had your list of medications to refer to. Went straight to the mark. Five hundred each for the ladies - sadly the gentleman must pay the full five thou as the car was taken out in his name. Pity, what? But all things considered, decent result. Release on payment. Address coming up, got a pen?'

Yes. Decent result. Very. But not so great for Karl, all things considered. Big fine to settle, wife's enjoyed a bit of a tupping in his absence, hire car stuck out in the serra awaiting collection if he manages to find it. Pity, what?

\*　　　\*　　　\*　　　\*

We're released from the hotel a few days early, it's needed as overspill for their own cases now. Fiona still on oxygen in Hueva - her Ken having found somewhere basic nearby, he must wait for the OK to move her. When the rest of us get back Lou and Karl have taken the first available flight and gone. I figure Anna still made two-fifty out of her discomfort. She won't have paid the boatman that's for sure, probably not her cousin either. I consider requesting a refund but decide maybe not, that puts her in my debt, I'll remind her of that sometime. The gang paid up for Lou's fine but there was some dragging of feet over Karl's. We settle things by chipping in on an individual discretion basis which raises about four hundred euros, not all in notes. So he was short of well over four grand. Maybe he'll think to hesitate before charging in, in future.

No. He won't.

Our helpful counter-people at the town hall hand over a bagful of keys and barely legible list of handwritten addresses. Fortunately I know a lady who knows where they are. Doesn't know who's in which but the gang won't have to mind a bit of a ramble through town with her. Lou's left our place tidy, all traces of prior activity nullified. Card on the table, to me: "The dragon sends his regards, and looks forward to meeting up again soon.."

Ellie: 'Dragon?'

'Ah… just a little souvenir we spotted in Pingo. Miscellany aisle. I bought it for her as a memento of our time together in lockdown.'

'Ahh. That's so sweet.'

## 14. TELEFONICA (Rondo) - SPAIN

May 15 2.15pm (log):

Telefonica ring ME on my mobile. I'm eating at a local restaurant with some friends and so surprised at this unheard of development that I push my chair back too quickly; its back legs catch on the unevenly tiled floor, I save myself from falling over backwards by grabbing the edge of the table but drop the phone in the process. It falls on the floor and the back flies off. When I put it to the side of my head again, the line is dead. The atmosphere during the rest of the meal is muted.

May 15 3.30pm (log):

Telefonica phone me again. I decide against referring to the earlier incident. The woman asks me for my address. I give it to her. She asks me if I am sure this is my address. Sensing trouble, I embark on the high risk strategy of attempting to explain to her that in fact we have two addresses, a postal address and an official address, which I know is ridiculous, but there it is, we didn't make the rules, it just so happens we have two addresses with two different postal codes and there isn't a fat lot we can do about it. Llagostera is our postal address and the postal code is 17240, but we are registered as residents of Santa Cristina for the purposes of all official documents, and the Santa Cristina code is 17244.

But look, it can't be too much of a problem because your blokes have already been here twice to deliver the poles, so they must know where we live, mustn't they? I say, trying to keep the doubt from out of my voice.

May 17 (log):

Telefonica on the blower again. This time it's a man and something tells me he's not from a call centre. I'm right. He's phoning from the Department of Analysis in Madrid, he tells me, and he'd like my address. I repeat my explanation of two days previously, giving myself higher marks for fluency this time. But you know all this already, surely. What's the problem? I ask him.

He tells me that, telephonically speaking, our address does not exist. His exact words (in translation of course, ha ha) are, Telephonically speaking, Sir, your address doesn't exist. It feels like a defining moment in this particular living-the-dream saga, and I wish I could think of a response to do it justice but not for the first time I cannot find the words to go with a situation. I content myself with a mildly daring, Mother of God, what do you want me to do?

Cometh the moment, cometh the man. Don't worry Sir, I have a plan. I see Baldrick relocated to a Telefonica office in Madrid. Why don't you go to your nearest neighbour who has a telephone and get his number. That way we'll be able to find you for sure.

I do Baldrick's bidding, in the process learning that when Señor Pons got his phone installed a decade or so ago it cost him a hundred and twenty thousand pesetas (about seven hundred and fifty euros) and we should think ourselves lucky we're getting ours for the normal connection fee of sixty euros. I concur, very heartily, and head back home to wait for Baldrick to phone me back, not believing for a moment that he will, for experience has taught me that nobody, but nobody, phones you back in Catalunya when they say they will. But Baldrick is made of a different metal and an hour later, right on cue, he calls as promised.

I tell him.

Right. Then: Is it really? He sounds genuinely interested. A few seconds of silence, followed by: That explains every-thing. More silence.

Everything? How?

Because your exchange is Bel Lloc, Señor Tysoe, not Santa Cristina. This is where the confusion was.

Very good. When will we get our phone?

Very soon, if there is nothing unforeseen. Your case is in my hands.

Su caso está en mis manos. This is the self-same phrase I remember David X using, and it sends a shiver down my spine. Before I can request name, rank and number he has put the phone down on me. Obviously an experienced campaigner.

May 28 2005 (email):

'I played another tennis match on Saturday in the grand-fathers' cup. I was winning 5 - 2 in the first set, and lost the match 7 - 5, 6 – 0. How can that happen, I ask myself?

At the weekend I bought a chain saw. This was a further step in the direction of becoming a relatively self-sufficient household on the outer margins of civilisation. We now have the wherewithal to meet much of our fuel needs for next winter. Good husbandry, or what? The vegetables are coming through as well – peppers, aubergines, beans, toms, spuds – all looking very healthy. My neighbour Francesc has taken it upon himself to train me in the ways of the land around here. He gave me some beans called

General Perons. It seems that after the second world war Argentina was one of the few countries that would trade with Spain. They sent over boat loads of meat and… yes, beans. Ever since, this particular variety of bean, which apparently runs like the clappers, has been known as General Peron.'

June 3 2.30pm (log):

Man in van draws up outside our house. I go to greet him. A glance through the rear windows of his vehicle reveals what looks suspiciously like several drums of telephone cable. There are extending ladders on the roof. Feel dizzy for a moment and have to clutch Man's shoulder to prevent myself falling. There is genuine concern in his eyes as he gently removes my hand and explains that this is just a reconnaissance mission, that he must now visit Bel Lloc to see the exchange which serves us, before he can go on with the installation. "Don't be long," I say as he drives off, doubtful of seeing him again. His smile lingers beyond his departure, like the Cheshire cat's.

It is a glorious, glorious summer's day. I look across the green fields and wooded slopes of our valley, shimmering in a heat haze, to the grey ridge of the Ardenys hills in the distance, and feel blessed.

Twice and three times blessed when Man returns in less than 30 minutes.

You've come back?

Yes.

Very good. Now you're…?

Well, I'm going to connect your telephone to the network by putting these cables here…

Wait a moment please. I feel very emotional, not to say confused. Completely irrationally, it suddenly seems to me a terrible problem that we don't actually have a telephone – an actual telephone, the thing you hold to your ear: should we already have bought one in preparation for this moment? Could our failure to have done so jeopardise this finely balanced situation? I start to try and explain this latest terrible fear I have. We don't have a telephone. I mean a real live telephone...

Somehow, miraculously, he knows how important this moment is, and he wants to help me. I am finally face to face with someone in whose hands I am happy for my case to be. Perhaps the emotion of it all is too much. I don't know because of course the moment is not recorded and I have no recollection other than of next being aware that Telefonica Man is pushing a flat cardboard box in my direction. It's in Telefonica's distinctive livery of yellow and blue, and there's a picture of a fancy new phone on the front, with many buttons and an LCD.

Is this our phone, do you mean? I say.

Yes, he says, smiling, still holding out the box.

Fantastic, I say, for it surely is, and anyway I can think of nothing else to say, but what I'm thinking is that amidst all the nonsense of the last eight months I'd never cast my mind forward to the interface between pre- and post-connection worlds, to thinking what it would be like, this Big Bang moment. I have an answer now, of sorts anyway. Within my grasp suddenly is a shiny white plastic phone packaged in yellow and blue, considerably more substantial than its ideal form, the only form I had considered up to now. It crosses my mind fleetingly that my relationship with Telefonica is at the point of moving beyond the

Platonic, and I am just not prepared for it. Is one ever, at such a moment?

*  *  *  *

Finally, July 6 2005, a group email to thirty or so of his friends, acquaintances and family.

'IT WAS A HISTORIC MOMENT.

Two evenings ago the information super highway extended a few more yards and reached into our home in this small corner of north-eastern Spain. At the point of connection I swear the birds in the garden fell silent for a moment. Who knows, but perhaps they were experiencing a sympathetic rippling of their plumage, or in their little bird-brains a fleeting sense of interconnectedness with distant relatives in unknown and unvisited lands? The great mysteries of Gaea are, after all, truly most mysterious.

Be that nonsense as it may, we are now in direct contact with one point three eight billion other inhabitants of this great planet of ours and that includes, of course, you. Nine months it has taken, almost to the day, for this to come about. During this time one or two matters of significance have taken place in various corners of the globe, but so far as we are concerned they have come and gone leaving ne'er a ripple whereas the central fact of lack of phone line has remained a constant throughout, dominating the land-scape of our lives as cathedrals towered over the world of the medieval peasant, blocking out the sun and condemning him or her to a life of ignorance and obfusca-tion.

The gestation has been long, frustrating, but also educational and character-building. "What does not kill me makes me stronger," as Nietzsche so aptly said – or was it

Jose Mourinho? There were times, terrible times, when the temptation to give up was almost too strong to bear, when it seemed easier to close one's eyes for the last time, roll over, and allow the dreadful monster Telefonica to stalk the land unfettered and unchallenged. But at these times, some small voice always succeeded in making itself heard. "No! Hold fast! Keep the faith!" And so it proved. Praise the Lord!

We have a number. It is 9728332827. When prefaced with 0034 and by means of the appropriate technology, both the spoken and written words, not to mention other symbols and images of fantastic complexity, can be precisely directed at our address from anywhere on the planet.

We are reborn!'

\*      \*      \*      \*